MW00618042

Cash Practice Success

How to See Half the Patients, Increase Your Income, Eliminate Insurance and Practice Medicine that Restores and Regenerates Health

By JR Burgess

Bestselling Author, CEO of Rejuv Medical and HealthOvators

FREE – Quiz & Strategy Call

This book includes a free 5 Practice Pillars quiz and 1:1 strategy call about your practice goals!

Get it NOW at
smartbizquiztribe.com/quiz/690

First edition | September 2018

ISBN 978-0-9801550-2-0 (paperback)

FOREWORD

Each of us has a calling. We have an inner drive that propels us to do, to become. I credit my mother for instilling the passion which drives me to help others. She taught me the impact of making others feel special and valued.

I began my career working for a large healthcare system where I saw as many patients as I could pack into my day. Sadly, I would meet with them for approximately ten minutes, give a quick diagnosis, then go on to the next patient. The quality of my services was clearly not optimal. I was prescribing medications to treat patients' metabolic disease or pain, without fully treating them in a manner which could create significant changes in their lives.

The necessity to build Rejuv Medical came from my frustration with the broken healthcare system and not being able to treat my patients in the manner they deserved. My vision was bigger than what was available in the community, which led me to the idea of creating a viable, profitable, scalable and sustainable model. I had no idea how I was going to do it!

Ten years ago, I contemplated moving from my hometown and leaving the healthcare agency I was practicing at for a larger community. Since I had a large patient base in my hometown, I decided to start my own practice and build the vision I was convinced the world needed.

I knew it was going to be tough. I have been good at getting successful outcomes for my patients, but business was new to me. Rejuv started out with the 'fearless threesome' - a nurse, a receptionist and myself. We were located in a small, 1,000 square foot space. I took the risk and used all my savings to launch my new practice. After three months, I had only a few hundred dollars left in my personal bank account. I did not pay myself a salary and there wasn't any profit. It came down to selling my house or getting a large loan. Thankfully, that very month, we received our first reimbursement check from Blue Cross. I still couldn't pay myself but at least my employees didn't have to find another job!

Still, my mind was not at ease because I wanted more than just getting my patients' joints and backs healed - I wanted to restore their vitality. I strongly believe we need to stop covering up symptoms and start treating the causes associated with each diagnosis. As a non-surgical and sports medicine specialist, I was the only doctor in Minnesota to start performing regenerative procedures such as Prolotherapy and Platelet Rich Plasma (PRP). My nurse was well-versed in hormone replacement therapy and balancing the endocrine system. Together, we started to evaluate hormones, adrenals, gastrointestinal health and micro-nutrient imbalances.

The rest of the medical community wasn't ready for regenerative therapy, yet we stood firm in what the research was showing us; research indicated the regeneration of degenerative painful joints and restoration of health to those suffering from debilitating chronic disease. Like other visionaries who were ahead of their time, we were ridiculed and called 'voodoo quacks', along with many other choice expletives. I can assure you that there is no comfort in being a pioneer, but now I can take pleasure in knowing that most of those naysayers have introduced regenerative or lifestyle changes into their practice.

Knowing the degenerating effects of having a poor diet, being overweight and not exercising have on the body, I felt compelled to teach and train patients on how to restore and achieve optimal health. Prescribing multiple medications is not a fix. Cortisone is a popular treatment for pain and inflammation, but it does not repair painful, arthritic knees, nor do diabetic medications reverse the disease. I was compelled to change the thoughts and behaviors of patients whose health and well-being had been diminished. It was time to abandon the band-aid approach to illness and focus on the restoration of health.

Being overweight puts added force on the body. Patients with bad knees felt helpless to change until they discovered losing weight would provide relief to an arthritic joint. Diabetic patients would continue to have life-threatening complications and dependency on medications if they did not lose weight and make positive lifestyle changes to reverse the disease. Practitioners tell their patients the importance of losing weight but, without support and education on healthy nutritional practices, few could implement positive changes. I needed a system to get my patients healthy, not just offer words of encouragement. I needed to assist them in restoring their health through movement, mindful eating and positive lifestyle changes in order to improve their outcome and regenerate their bodies.

The right treatments, health professionals and the patients' willingness to make positive change could combine to use the body's natural ability to heal and could restore and regenerate health. Utilizing a care team consisting of physicians, advanced care providers, physical therapists, dietitians, exercise specialists and health coaches, we could impact the way the health system operates and decrease the rise in chronic diseases. My ultimate goal would combine the science of medicine with the physiology and endocrinology of the body. I felt a team approach that would create permanent changes and regeneration in patients' lives was possible.

This belief led me on a quest to find my next team member. I envisioned someone who shared my dreams, passions and beliefs, and who could be a gatekeeper for meeting patients' needs while growing the practice into a reproducible model. I imagined a business visionary who was equally as passionate and eager to create as massive of an impact as I was - fortunately, I found him on my exam table! During our first conversation, I was excited to find someone with a mutual vision.

JR Burgess was a personal trainer at a well-known gym where I worked out. His athleticism, which included rugby, resulted in injuries that plagued him for years; as a result, I began treating him with prolotherapy. He had just finished graduate school in sports management and talked about his desire to help people lose weight. He cited the new series, *The Biggest Loser*, and felt he could replicate it on a larger scale in clinics across the world. He saw the gap in healthcare and believed he could bridge the gap between fitness and medicine to the extent that it would change the global paradigm. He understood my vision and mission, which resulted in him becoming the fourth employee and my eventual (current) business partner in Rejuv. We now have another location and two other companies aimed at helping redefine the way healthcare can be delivered.

After hiring JR, we converted an exam room into a small gym where we taught and encouraged patients to eat healthy and exercise. We began to see results and our patient testimonies were powerful, dramatic and inspirational. Not only did they experience less pain in their joints, but they had more energy and zest. My value to do things the right way and the positive feedback I was getting from patients was all the fuel I needed to keep pushing forward.

We built a state-of-the art building - 28,000 square feet - but lost over a third of our insurance contracts. We were given the option to stop doing stem cell treatments, PRP (Plasma Rich Platelet) therapies, and functional medicine if we wanted to remain In-network; that was an easy no. I would risk losing everything rather than go back to my former way of practicing. I now believe the old way I was treating patients did more harm than good in regard to treating pain and chronic diseases.

Rather than losing it all, we came together as a team in order to survive. Not only did we have to show great outcomes, but we needed to be leaders. Without insurance contracts, we had to become even better at marketing directly to consumers. We had to be creative in designing an amazing experience for our patients that was efficient, results-driven and repeatable. We needed to grow to another level in a hurry, or the business would fail - along with our dreams and aspirations. After overcoming our emotional and financial stresses, we created the company MedFit. It was the beginning of sharing our treatment model with the world.

We have come a long way yet, in some ways, we have just started. We successfully created the kind of practice I dreamed of, and we are changing healthcare practices around the world with our model. In spite of our success, we have not fixed the healthcare crisis. We understand it cannot be done alone; the world needs more HealthOvators (our third company brand name) and medical leaders who put people before profits.

In the last nine years, we have grown and expanded our services. We are building the momentum for a viable and long-lasting model that will help society rebound from the current healthcare crisis. We are proud to have gone from a four-person team to 82 members. Our team is talented and passionate about healthcare. They share our mission to help change lives permanently and positively.

Our model is proven and can be implemented into your practice as well. You, too, can make an impact, change lives and practice in the manner you believe is best for your patients.

Rejuv is our own testing laboratory where we innovate and share our model with other practitioners. I envision the standard medical model of treating patients with medications and not impacting health and longevity a thing of the past. I have seen amazing results from treating our patients with PRP, stem cell injections, hormones, exercise and weight loss. These treatments are all backed by sound scientific research. Traditional medical models are not going away any time soon, yet there are millions of people who want to live to their full potential and are seeking cash-pay alternatives to restore their health.

We are pioneers and leaders in teaching the necessary medical skills and the business of regenerative medicine, functional medicine and medical fitness. We are aware of changing trends but stick to the systems and foundations that are solid and tested.

You have the ability to affect the lives of those you encounter. Every conversation, encounter or even a passing hello is an opportunity to create a positive experience for those who entrust us for their care. The contributions and the work you do to make the world a better place is highly valued.

We wouldn't be where we are today without participating in masterminds and without investing in ourselves, our team, and paying for speed by buying systems and coaching in the areas where we proactively chose to develop expertise. If you have the desire to build a successful healthcare practice and believe that the current system is broken, I encourage you to become part of the HealthOvators community. Together, we are changing lives - we are Innovating Health and Wealth for quality of life and more freedom for our patients, our families and our communities.

With Much Respect,

Joel Baumgartner, M.D.

Co-Founder of Rejuv Medical, MedFit and HealthOvators

Pioneer and Leader in Regenerative Healthcare

Table of Contents

INTRODUCTION

This book is for physicians, practice owners and wellness professionals who want cash-pay services such as regenerative medicine, functional medicine, weight loss and lifestyle medicine, to help restore and regenerate health without drugs and surgery. The goal is simple: to help you understand the framework of how to build a seven-figure plus cash practice with "The Five Pillars of Practice Success Platform."

We support physicians and medical professionals in building a proven new model of healthcare that is outcome-driven, affordable, sustainable, profitable and desperately needed to help patients restore and regenerate health.

Sound too good to be true? The vision is real. You really can see half the patients while earning more income, without dealing with insurance, bureaucracy or red tape, in a business model that enables getting paid faster and empowers practicing life-changing medicine vs. simply covering up problems.

How do we know? We've proven the business model both in our own business and in more than 60 of our physician client practices around the world through HealthOvators and the MedFit Team. They are now enjoying new levels of income, impact and freedom through this unique approach that is completely redefining healthcare.

Next-Level Health Needs a Next-Level Business Model

We are on a mission to redefine healthcare. We have invested millions into designing, implementing and refining this model and want to succeed with you - the visionary and independent thinker who is choosing to create a medical practice or wellness center that's focused on delivering remarkable outcomes. This is about building a practice dedicated to changing the lives of the patients and community you serve.

Our 28,000 sq. feet Integrated Health Center is an operational flagship that demonstrates what we believe is the new reality of sustainable healthcare for visionary physicians who understand that now is the time to create next-level health and wellness for patients.

That's why we broke down every system, process and protocol - so physicians and practitioners like you can replicate our patient and business success. I am going to share a unique approach to completely change the face of healthcare. I want to provide you with the structure it takes to run a successful cash practice. The ultimate goal is to eliminate pain and reverse, or better manage, chronic diseases, which include diabetes, heart disease, arthritis and body degeneration.

I often speak and network at medical conferences that allow me the opportunity to partner with doctors and other medical professionals regarding the healthcare crisis. The first question I ask is, "*How many of you feel there is an immediate answer to solving the healthcare crisis we face today?*" Typically, there is no answer to the question and there is little confidence in finding solutions. Finger-pointing is easier than exploring solutions for fixing the problems.

With our research, resources and proven system, we are able to reach those who see possibilities. We strongly believe we can redefine healthcare by restoring health and rebuilding our body using its own ability to heal, without drugs or surgery, as the first line of treatment.

As the father of four children, I want to create a solid foundation in which my family can live and thrive. Within the healthcare industry, it is pivotal to construct a holistic solution, which takes into account the mental and social factors of a person rather than just treating the physical symptoms of a disease. Although the system appears stacked against us, I chose this profession to help people.

Together we can redefine the healthcare system with measurable outcomes that improve the quality of life for our patient. Healthcare professionals generally enter the field with a desire to help others and with a spirit of inquiry. Now, you are the key to change. Your frustration with the current system, which is set up for big government, big pharma, insurance payors and profit before people, does not have to be standard practice. Rather than supporting the current system, which is stagnant, it's time to spread your wings and develop a new paradigm that is sensible and creative.

Physicians are pressured to see more patients, which leads to burnout and job dissatisfaction. If you are one of the healthcare professionals seeing hundreds of patients a week, prescribing medications that are not helping and maybe even making matters worse, spending more time charting than listening, and trying to assist patients in making positive changes but are then stymied by reimbursement cuts, you may want to consider entering into our model of practice.

There is hope and there are solutions. Our model will provide you the income and freedom to reverse and better manage chronic diseases including diabetes, heart disease, arthritis, chronic pain and body degeneration, while optimizing your patient's health, resulting in more vibrancy, pep and gusto. We have made many mistakes along the way in making this model profitable; yet we have created a predictable, consistent and repeatable system, which is necessary for the sustainability of our visionary healthcare system. We are excited to share this unique approach, which will completely change the current healthcare paradigm. It is our hope you will join us in fulfilling our vision.

I want you to visualize seeing half the number of patients, earning more income and eliminating insurance bureaucracy, while practicing medicine that restores and regenerates health. Does it sound too good to be true? It's real - we did it and so can you! Learning and implementing The Five Pillars made our practice at Rejuv successful. The

Five Pillars are designed to provide you with the foundation and structure to be innovative and passionate while creating lasting beneficial effect with and for your patients.

I will share more about the position we are in as a society and provide information about how we are redefining healthcare. We have not designed this book as a standard medical journal, with sources attached. If you are interested in the research and medical evidence of our model, Dr. Joel Baumgartner has written the best-selling book, _Regenerate: How To Restore and Regenerate Health Without Drugs and Surgery_. My plan is to give you the business structure and mindset necessary for cash practice success.

The Shift is Happening

We are starting to see a unique shift in the healthcare environment. Rather than being ridiculed by the standard medical model, Rejuv has compiled a substantial amount of data supporting our practice methods. Our goal was never to win a literary award, but to give you the quickest and simplest overview of the lessons learned, and the wisdom attained by redefining healthcare. We have confidence that this model will give you hope, show you possibilities, and provide you the framework, structure and systems you need to have to achieve the same outcome.

Obesity, illness, disease, and prescription use continues to rise. Healthcare is not affordable, and it continues to increase, while reimbursements are decreasing. Bundled payments, outcome-based quality measures, and managed care are the only solutions being proposed, which lead to more regulations, red tape and bureaucracy. Analysis of prescription-dispensing trends show seven of the top ten medications are for preventable, lifestyle-related diseases.

If you want to know what they are, here is the list: Hydrocodone (pain medication), Generic Zocor (a cholesterol-lowering statin drug prescription), Lisinopril (a blood pressure drug), Generic Synthroid (Thyroid medication), Generic Norvasc (an angina/blood pressure drug), Generic Prilosec (an antacid drug), Azithromycin (an antibiotic), Amoxicillin (an antibiotic), Generic Glucophage (a diabetes drug) and Hydrochlorothiazide (a water pill used to lower blood pressure).

Obesity is a primary factor contributing to disease and chronic pain. It is estimated that within the next five years, one in two people will be obese (rather than the current rate of one in three). It is also the leading cause of preventable death. The American Medical Association now considers obesity a disease.

In 2008, a Kaiser Family Foundation study disclosed that physical inactivity was costing the U.S. healthcare system over $102 billion annually. Throughout 2010, prescription drug spending in United States was $259 billion, which is predicted to double in the next five years. Obesity impacts the outcome of surgical procedures, resulting in longer operating times in comparison to non-obese patients and an increase in post-operative complications.

According to the 2010 UTHealth graph, by 2020 the United States will have the greatest explosion of obesity in the nation's history. The westernized diet and a decrease in physical activity is to blame. Inactivity is so detrimental to one's health that sitting is referred to as the new smoking.

The American Diabetes Association completed a study between 1996 and 2007, when the obesity rates were soaring. The percentage of people receiving advice on weight, diet and exercise from primary care physicians dropped by 41 percent. Unfortunately, those in greatest need, with conditions such as hypertension, diabetes or metabolic syndrome, were given less support and information. The Journal of the American Board of Family Medicine found as little as 29 to 42 percent of overweight or obese patients reported being counseled by their physicians. These studies point out the gaps in our current healthcare model.

Four years ago, a prominent community member joined our medical fitness program. Due to being morbidly obese and having serious risk factors, I scheduled him for a stress test and a sleep lab evaluation to determine if he suffered from sleep apnea. Within minutes of starting the test, a nurse ordered a Continuous Positive Airway Pressure (CPAP) machine. When the patient told me about his appointment, I commented, "*I bet your physician was pleased to hear you were joining our program after he told you CPAP may no longer be needed if you lost significant weight?*" His response was not what I expected. He stated his physician had not mentioned exercise or diet at all! I was disappointed to hear that since the only solution for him was changing his diet and losing weight. Instead, his problems were ignored by this physician. This is not providing quality healthcare but is merely placing a band-aid on a festering wound. I finally realized how broken the system truly is with glaring clarity.

Our nation has advanced greatly when it comes to emergency and traumatic care, along with communicable diseases, but the system has failed miserably when it pertains to chronic disease and pain management. Innovation and progression is present in nearly every aspect of our nation's infrastructure except medicine. My only understanding is that this unfortunate situation is the result of greed from those who control the current standard of care.

According to the American Medical Association, patients have a better understanding of their health risks and are three times more motivated to attempt weight loss when their physicians counsel them. Physicians are seen as authority figures, and the power of authority creates conformity even when people attempt to resist change. As a former personal trainer, I knew an integrated approach to weight loss was, and still is, necessary to change a person's attitude. In additional to the nutritional component, the psychological aspects are equally, if not more, important.

When "*The Biggest Loser*" show first aired, a physician informed the contestants of their health risks and at what age their health status placed them. For example, "*Mrs.*

Jones, if you do not start eating better and changing your habits, you are at high risk for having a stroke, heart attack, or death". The contestant would cry when faced with the reality of her condition. Our system of pharmaceuticals as the solution insulates us from facing the truth and aids in the continuation of an unhealthy lifestyle. It is our job, and a responsibility and an expectation as providers, to educate patients on the risks they face regarding metabolic-related diseases and to provide them with alternatives.

A physician's role in weight loss is monumental. The Diabetes Educator compiled a patient survey. Eighty-six percent of obese patients expressed a desire to lose weight and 62% thought their physician could help. For years, the weight loss industry has been thriving, yet obesity rates continue to rise. Rather than the quick panacea people are hoping for as a solution, more effective and realistic solutions are needed.

With Knowledge Comes Power - And Responsibility

In 2011, Pamela Kufahl, Editor-in-Chief, Club Industry, estimated that in the next ten years, every healthcare organization will need a facility and program dedicated to the prevention and treatment of poor lifestyle-related diseases.

At Rejuv, we felt an obligation to put together a medically-integrated, safe and progressive program. When you are seeing a patient, whether they have autoimmune disorder, pain, sickness, injury or chronic disease, the solution is to uncover the root cause of their medical problem. Obese patients feel embarrassed and ashamed of their weight. In caring for patients, we need to talk clearly and respectfully with them. We need to obtain their history, take their vital signs, get their weight, height and help them develop confidence in their ability to begin an exercise program.

When screening patients, I ask two questions, "*On average, how many days per week do you engage in moderate to strenuous exercise such as a brisk walk or swimming?*" The next question is, "*On average, how many minutes do you engage in exercise at this level?*" The goal is 150 minutes per week, or 21.4 minutes a day, of moderate to intense activity. If a patient has a sedentary lifestyle, we start with light activity, then progress forward while affirming and encouraging change.

Exercise, nutrition and lifestyle changes are the solutions. Other professionals may debate that obesity and chronic disease are different from chronic pain, injuries and arthritis, yet many disorders are controllable while others are not. Inflammation, a sedentary lifestyle, being overweight, poor eating habits, sleep deprivation, etc., lead to recurring chronic pain and injuries.

On average, 100 million Americans suffer from chronic pain and 22% of primary care visits are for pain management. Chronic pain costs the United States $635 billion annually with $18 billion being spent on pain medications. These costs are more than cancer, heart disease and diabetes combined. Opioids are often used by doctors to treat chronic pain, but overuse has become endemic. The FDA states, "*Opioids pose a serious risk of overuse, abuse, overdose, and death.*" Opioid overdoses is now the leading cause of accidental death. To combat addiction and accidental death, the United States is focused on providing better, non-opioid pain options, such as CBD (cannabidiol) oil or medical marijuana.

A primary treatment for chronic pain is analgesic medication and cortisone injections. Both provide dramatic relief, but it is only temporary. The use of analgesics and cortisone creates a vicious cycle in which the patient seeks additional medication to relieve symptoms. More medication can result in addiction, organ damage and an increase in the degenerated joint process. Evidence-based practice has documented the negative effects of steroid injections. The Orthopedic Journal of Sports Medicine, May 2015, states, "*Steroids have a dose dependent effect.*" Low doses have shown beneficial effects in pain reduction and mobility, but high doses are associated with gross cartilage damage.

Surgery is another commonly utilized option in which some patients end up in worse shape post-surgery. Many patients have been negatively impacted or destroyed by using surgery as the first step instead of the last option. My mother had surgery for a simple foot procedure that caused her more pain and limitation. Subsequently, she had two more procedures in an attempt to fix the first one, but she had little improvement. Her large toe now points upward, she cannot wear most shoes, her ability to walk is limited and she has ongoing pain. We do nerve blocks to reduce her pain, but the damage done by surgery is permanent.

Our role as healers should be to treat obesity, diabetes and metabolic syndrome with proper nutrition and exercise and to utilize medication only when absolutely necessary. If medication is required, it needs to be on a short-term basis. For pain, with arthritis and degeneration, the goal is to restore, rebuild function and regenerate tissue. We cannot continue to ignore the evidence and offer more steroids, pain medications or surgery as the first line of treatment. We have treated many insulin-resistant patients and were able to normalize their blood glucose levels without the use of medication. In addition to exercise, which includes mild resistance training and elevated heart rate training, nutritional intervention that directly targets a cellular response to secrete insulin is necessary.

I cannot stress enough that the rising costs of medical care has to cease. In 2006, several economists and financial projectors understood the housing market was in a 'bubble,' but it was going to eventually fail. They communicated, did their job, it was well-documented - then the market imploded in 2007; excessive risk-taking became pervasive throughout the housing system. Homeowners lost a cumulative of $3.3 trillion in home equity and, in 2008, the stock market erased $6.9 trillion in shareholder wealth. The same can happen in the healthcare industry. The question is, will things get worse before they get better? Only time will tell.

The Leading Edge of Lifestyle Medicine

Regenerative, functional and lifestyle medicine has substantially increased in the last ten years. Among U.S. adults, more than 90% of type 2 diabetes, 80% of CAD (coronary artery disease), 70% of stroke, and 70% of colon cancer are potentially preventable by a combination of non-smoking, avoidance of being overweight, moderate physical activity, healthy diet and moderate alcohol consumption. Each year, nearly 900,000 Americans die prematurely from the five leading causes of death (heart disease, cancer, unintentional injuries, stroke and chronic respiratory disease), which are preventable! Making positive changes in personal behavior drastically reduces the risk of premature death. As healthcare professionals, we need to rally and target the root causes while decreasing cost and improving patient care.

There is rise in chronic disease as the massive generation of Baby Boomers (1946 -1964) retire. The growth in the number of elderly patients will put pressure on the already stressed healthcare system. The current healthcare system is not designed to assess, prevent, diagnose, postpone or treat multiple chronic conditions. In 2018, the Centers for Medicare & Medicaid Services (CMS) programs implemented the Diabetes Prevention Program. For the first time, insurance companies began paying for preventative and wellness services, such as fitness training, health coaching, nutritional counseling, massage, weight loss, chiropractic care, stress management and other low-cost medical services, which help reduce the rise of chronic diseases. If the program is proven effective, it is predicted that these services will be adopted to many private payers. Our only question to the program is: when it is fully covered, will people value their health the same if they don't have to pay for it? The good news it will provide more access for those willing to do the work to take control of their health.

We control our lives. If we carry extra body weight, fail to eat nutritiously, are inactive, smoke or do drugs, we fail our bodies. These are all factors that are controllable by each individual. Another controllable factor is stress. Stress can affect our body, thoughts, feelings and behavior. If stress is not controlled, it contributes to health problems, such as high blood pressure, obesity, heart disease and diabetes.

Emotionally, extreme stress can lead to anxiety, depression, irritability, eating disorders, feelings of inadequacy, drug and alcohol abuse, etc. Stress can be managed by learning cognitive-behavioral techniques, participating in meditation and relaxation, practicing yoga, being physically active, taking breaks, having fun, spirituality, maintaining a social circle and support network.

What else is controllable? Our endocrine and nutrient imbalances can be diagnosed and properly managed. There is significant data citing genetic influences since a large number of genes each play a role in determining our personality, health and well-being. Genetic research shows our choices aren't always ours. Taking a close look at epigenetics, we pass down some of these expressions from the life we choose to live. We're passing down to our children a deck of cards that is stacked against them if we are not taking self-responsibility in our lives. Mostly uncontrollable factors are natural age progression and accidents. For example, if I was rear-ended while driving, the trauma to tissue could be in the form of nerve, joint and bone damage and instability.

We have learned to communicate to our patients that they have the answer to their health issues. They are given structure, motivation, support, accountability and community but, ultimately, it is up to them to implement and sustain change. We devise customized fitness routines and eating plans to support each client based on their genetics, preferences and resources and, if they have movement imbalances, physical therapy and corrective exercise are prescribed. Using functional medicine, we work at controlling their inflammation and eliminating toxins within their bodies. We balance bio-identical hormones and optimize micronutrients and microbiome.

We teach the importance of getting proper sleep for recovery, provide resources and education on communication and coping skills, and spiritual or meditative techniques to reduce stress. Once health is restored, we can truly regenerate the degenerated tissue with nerve treatments, sweet caudal epidurals and hydrodissection of entrapped nerves. Prolotherapy, TENEX, PRP and the power of stem cells are the treatment options used to regenerate our bodies once measures have been taken to restore basic health.

CHAPTER 1: HOW A MEDICAL VISIONARY AND BUSINESS VISIONARY CAME TOGETHER TO INNOVATE AND REDEFINE HEALTHCARE

While in graduate school, I worked as a personal trainer. I loved coaching and helping people lose weight. At a young age, I started competing in sports and instructing my teammates on how to improve their playing while gaining better understanding of the strategies. Sports is how I dealt with depression and strong emotions. They were my healthy outlet (sublimation).

After completing high school, I went to a community college (I was not accepted into a University since I barely graduated from high school). In college, I played division one rugby and baseball. After completing my undergraduate degree, I continued playing sports but my knee became increasingly painful. I was thirty years old and already had four knee surgeries. I continued to play rugby on the weekends but had a constant, painful limp. I was ready to give up rugby, but the aggressive and competitive aspect of the sport was my greatest relief and outlet for handling my emotions.

I decided to consult with Dr. Baumgartner, a family practice and sports medicine doctor, after hearing the results from a personal training client of mine who had Type 1 diabetes and a torn rotator cuff. He told me about the Prolotherapy and PRP injections he was receiving from Dr. Baumgartner.

After just two treatments, he was completely healed. Although his treatments occurred two years earlier, I was training him without limitations. He had no indication of a previously torn rotator cuff and had completely restored function and strength. I called Dr. Baumgartner since physical therapy, cortisone shots, drugs, bracing and multiple surgeries were not effective. I researched Dr. Baumgartner and discovered he was a pioneer in the regenerative medicine field. He authored the primary book on prolotherapy techniques, a book that physicians around the world are using to perform non-surgical treatments.

At Rejuv, Dr. Baumgartner explained that he is a family practice physician who did a fellowship in sports medicine and was passionate about providing innovative procedures that were safe, minimally invasive and effective at eliminating - or drastically reducing - pain and injuries without drugs or surgery. He stated, "*JR, because you eat healthy and exercise, you are likely to get a better outcome. I would like to run labs in case your thyroid, Vitamin D or testosterone levels are off. This way we can make sure we do what we can to help optimize your results.*" He explained, if his patient is diabetic and on Metformin, it is covering up the root problem. Likewise, if a patient has degenerative disc disease and I cannot get him to engage in healthy, active living and maintain a healthy body composition, I am not helping them long-term. "*I'm all-in on innovating a model of care that fixes the cover-ups for those who are looking to live their best life possible. I need someone to help run my business and add the lifestyle and preventative medicine component as a concierge to my patients*," he stated.

I was watching '*The Biggest Loser*,' imagining it as my dream job. I thought, '*if only I could lock people in a cabin for a month, I could help them overcome their unhealthy lifestyles and change their new behaviors until it became habitual.*' Dr. Baumgartner said he was willing to take any measures possible to make it happen, but he needed help completing his model. He also needed someone to help grow his vision of changing the world of healthcare.

Marketing and attracting clients is not his forte, although the majority of his clientele were receiving cash-paid procedures. His desire is to be a physician, not a salesperson, and he did not have business management experience.

Growing up, Dr. Baumgartner was an individual sport star athlete. He was confident in building his medical vision, which he wanted to focus on rather than learning to run the business. Integrative care is his passion and vision for changing healthcare. I was very excited about the conversation. Our visions matched and, since I was no longer limping and felt great, I became an instant believer in what he was doing.

Only Ten Percent - But They Were A Start

Dr. Baumgartner offered me a position as the Medical Fitness Director, but he would have to wait since I had a six-month commitment with my current employer. Additionally, I was going from a six figure plus income, building water towers, to just $45k in Dr. Baumgartner's newly formed practice. I felt blessed with the opportunity to get results for his patients while growing a business model that I knew was needed. In January of 2010, I starting working in an 80 square foot office in a 1,000 square foot clinic. I thought I was going to be a concierge to all the patients, but quickly discovered that only ten percent genuinely want to be healed and made sustainably better. Patients came looking for immediate relief from their pain and did not want exercise to be a part of that equation.

This taught me how to market externally, outside of our facility. Previously, we were only doing newspaper articles before I learned the skills of marketing and advertising. Then, in walked Susan. She had severe, chronic pain, had put on more than fifty pounds due to limited mobility and was subsequently depressed. At her worst, she contemplated suicide. She was on seventeen medications and had seven joint replacements. Her surgeon informed her there was nothing else - her pain specialist would not give her any more analgesics. She already felt like a zombie and didn't want medications to be long-term solutions.

When she came in, I said, "*Susan, I don't know that I'm equipped to help you*". However, I referred her to Dr. Baumgartner. He evaluated and planned to treat her with PRP, after he was able to optimize some of her health. He referred her to our Functional Medicine Department, with labs and nutraceuticals recommended to optimize her thyroid, nutrients and Vitamin D levels. She started physical therapy, so we could work her joints. I provided corrective exercises and coached her on nutritional recommendations that fit her lifestyle. Three months later, she lost fifty pounds and was taken off two of her medications. The best part was she got her zest and vitality back.

Susan was grateful that we helped her change her life; over time, she referred more than fifty clients to our practice. To this day, Susan continues to be a patient in our lifestyle and functional medicine program.

Susan's success was an exciting moment for us. We realized we are operating regenerative healthcare and providing hope and solutions for those who had little hope and were desperate for help. That was our 'A-ha!' moment - if we could get more people to focus and improve on all three of these areas (nutrition, movement and positive lifestyle changes), we could truly reverse conditions such as chronic pain and disease. We could do this by integrating our three-step system that provides predictable, consistent and repeatable results when fully experienced.

We created a patient experience map that focused on the three aspects of our model. Restoring health with fitness and lifestyle change; rebuilding the body with regenerative orthopedics, physical therapy and bracing; and rejuvenating clients' internal health with functional medicine, IV therapies and bio-identical hormones. We began getting amazing results and outcomes for hundreds of people in our community and became known as the place to go to change your life!

To grow the practice faster, we went to several high-level coaching programs. Once we learned how to market appropriately, our fitness program was rewarded with hundreds of new patients a month. That allowed us to grow from an 80 to 6,000 square foot gym in less than a year. We were not just growing our gym but also our clinic.

We learned a two-step integration system that assisted over 50 percent of our patients enter directly into our clinic system when they came to lose weight. These individuals were amazing patients for our providers because they were motivated to change, and willing to exercise and eat better. Those factors made the outcomes stronger as opposed to patients who want immediate results to eliminate pain or disease but are not willing to do the work for the best outcomes.

Due to positive outcomes, we started getting more attention although we were still viewed as being outside-the-box by our competitors. In 2011, we started designing a state-of-the-art, 28,000 square foot integrated center. At that time, it was one of the largest independently-owned and integrated centers in the world.

Since we were still viewed as being unconventional by competitors, other networks were calling and complaining to the board about our practice techniques. In 2011, few clinics were offering stem cell procedures; functional medicine was considered voodoo treatment. Therefore, the insurance companies decided to drop us from coverage if we continued practicing regenerative medicine. Since Dr. Baumgartner saw outcomes far too significant to ignore, he continued to practice what he believed to be right by his patients.

By 2012, I was the practice administrator and Chief Financial Officer (CFO) of Rejuv. I was overwhelmed, wondering how we could afford the new building we were to start using in early 2013. We had lost a third of our contracts and, with that, nearly a third of our revenue. I had no idea how we were going to sustain the business. We decided to keep our focus on learning how to attract our ideal patients and delivering unmatched outcomes.

By this time, we had built an amazing community reputation. We even started seeing community leaders, celebrities, professional athletes, former Olympians and Minnesota Vikings players. One former Vikings player, currently a sideline-announcer, came to Rejuv after hearing about us from another player.

He had recently retired from the NFL and suffered from osteoarthritis, digestive difficulties from the countless protein drinks, and numerous pain pills he had taken to manage the rigor of ten consecutive NFL seasons. Chronic pain was his new norm, yet he was frustrated because his workouts were limited due to knee pain. He completed functional medicine tests and had bloodwork done.

Afterward, we introduced the right supplements, eliminated inflammatory foods, extracted stem cells from his bone marrow and transplanted them into his knees. Two months later, while walking his dog, it started raining so he impulsively took off running for home. Within seconds he realized he was pain-free for the first time in a decade. He decided to keep running and felt a 'running high' that he had not experienced in years. He continues to make progress and has promoted us on his radio program. Others now realize our leading-edge solutions are working.

Traveling around the world, we had opportunities to meet industry leaders and celebrity influencers. At a busy conference, I met Mike Koenigs who is a digital media celebrity who helps professionals get their business message seen, heard and found. During a presentation at a seminar I was attending, he talked about having chronic shoulder pain and being a cancer survivor. I let him know we could help if he was willing to speak to our doctors. His primary concern was about downtime, since he frequently traveled and speaking on stage was his source of income. I informed him he would only need to be in a brace for a few days and could have the procedure done the morning before he spoke on the stage in the afternoon.

The procedure and his talk went great! After a couple of weeks, Mike was without pain for the first time. He was able to sleep on his shoulder, the popping symptoms stopped and he began his favorite exercise, swimming. Mike was back on top of his game, bringing this energy and celebrity power back onstage. He has been influential in our business and is now working on leading other doctors in changing the course of healthcare based on his experiences in functional and regenerative medicine.

Leaders in Unconventional, Transformational Healthcare

Amongst the innovative medical community, we are leaders in providing unconventional healthcare which has our community raving about their transformations. Rejuv Medical was the recipient of the 2015 Central Minnesota Innovation Award. Our video and design of our integrated facility can be seen on YouTube under 'Rejuv Medical Innovation Summit Award'.

It was a proud moment for our team, especially since it is hard being ridiculed when you know you have something special. Times change and now all the medical facilities in our community are doing regenerative medicine. Historically, pioneers were - at one time - looked at as being crazy! No conformist has ever made history. We continue to prove that daily.

Three years into starting our journey, we created MedFit. By 2016, we helped thirty locations implement our medical fitness and regenerative model and have grown internationally in Taiwan, China and Canada. We believe healthcare without fitness, nutritional support and health coaching is sick care. When designed correctly, we knew medical fitness and lifestyle medicine could be added to any healthcare model such as: specialty clinics; hospitals; physical therapy centers; chiropractic clinics; naturopath clinics; stand-alone gyms; companies offering corporate wellness; and family practice models.

We have traveled around the world to share our vision and my book, 'The Medical Fitness Impact Plan,' which teaches our system, and is based on the premise that exercise and lifestyle coaching are the foundations to restoring health and medicine. The Medical Fitness Impact Plan became a number one bestselling book.

We realized our affiliates needed a structured plan to make their practices successful before they added medical fitness and lifestyle medicine. Only 20% of the clinics were adding medical fitness and having the same type of impact that we have created. Many were happy to provide a solution for helping their patients, but not enough were seeing profits. Medical fitness was not the primary driver for their business the way it has been for us. I learned there were some unique assets, like Dr. Baumgartner and myself as drivers in the business, but as much as I tried to teach or give our turnkey processes, these doctors and trainers did not have the skills or the confidence to replicate the same results.

The Pivot Point

That's when we pivoted and started teaching the business strategies, personal development and marketing skills necessary to grow each practices' core focus first. If we told people what to do - and even gave them our exact systems - and they were not were not proactive in implementing the changes needed, the results could not be duplicated. That's why we created HealthOvators and our MasterMind program two and a half years ago. We needed a mastermind that taught practitioners how to run a successful practice and grow their skills. If they hired a personal trainer who was on a virtual island by themselves and didn't have the doctor who owned the practice participating in the systems, it would not produce the same results. They were not integrating on the same level we had and operated like hospital wellness centers working in silos.

Our success was predicated on the integration, teamwork and relentless effort of growth in all areas of practice. Once we identified the gap, we created "**The Five Pillars of Practice Success Platform.**" This has enabled us to provide much greater success for our affiliates. Now we have realistic and very achievable goals of helping other medical professionals and practice owners have the same impact in their businesses.

The Summit Has Been A Game-Changer

Four years ago, we created the Regenerative Business Summit and this year, for the first time, we have changed the name to Cash Practice Success Summit because we no longer are just attracting regenerative medicine and sports medicine doctors. We are bringing together medical professionals who are in search of cash practice success and integrated models of care. We started having more and more success when we were helping people understand and learn the practice management skills to make their practice successful.

Recently, we signed a 100-location license deal in China, as we are now far more confident in our systems and training to help practitioners join us in the mission to redefine healthcare. I wish we could offer guarantees but there is still an obligation to do the work, grow your skills and develop your team as you, ultimately, decide your own level of success. But we know we can provide you the structure, support, systems, community and accountability that helps position you for massive success in your own healthcare practice or wellness center.

I feel it is very important to not oversell patients or medical professionals on guaranteed outcomes as how each person takes action dictates their success. For example, I ask our patient affiliates to be very objective about their experiences in our programs. Dr. Rank and his wife, Linda, Physician Assistant, were willing to provide a testimonial to this nature.

Dr. Rank stated, "*I am an ER physician frustrated by the current healthcare system. I always thought that health and fitness could prevent chronic illness, but this was before I had ever heard about functional medicine. Looking for inspiration, I went to a functional medicine conference and met the team at MedFit who had a blueprint for the type of practice I wanted to have. They provide a template for running a practice and training on how to market and attract patients. They have practical workshops for* regenerative medicine training. Also, regular business coaching to keep you on track for success."

Linda wrote, "*What we didn't know we would get out of the MasterMind is genuine friendships with like-minded people. You develop a bond with the other attendees as well and share our experiences and information. The experience with the Practice Success MasterMind has truly impacted our lives and businesses on many levels. My only regret is that I wasted time to join. In business, mistakes can be costly and emotionally draining. It's been a relief to have people on our side to help guide us from their own personal experience.*"

Last year, Dr. John Tait, M.D., one of our first clients, won our Regenerative Practitioner of the Year Award. He was one of our first clients five years ago when we started MedFit. Prior to becoming our client, Dr. Tait was forced to see hundreds of patients at his pain management practice and was prescribing only drugs or cover-ups. He felt he was hurting patients long-term more than he was helping them in the short-term. He only continued to see reimbursement cuts for the procedures he was providing his patients. Denials were becoming commonplace and he was frustrated for not getting paid for services rendered.

These changes were affecting his income because he was on a production model, so he was tired of the red tape and bureaucracy of insurance systems. Unfortunately, he didn't have any business experience, nor did he know enough about marketing to attract cash-paying patients. Initially, he lacked the confidence in starting his own clinic.

I met Dr. Tait at the Fitness Business Summit. I happened to sit next to him, the only physician at the event. He told me he was considering leaving his job as a physician to become a personal trainer. He also wanted to deliver the meal plan he created that he believed could help reduce inflammation and help people lose weight and reduce pain naturally. I started telling him about our model.

After numerous conversations, coming to visit our practice, and putting together a solid, structured plan, he was able to start his own practice. Now, Dr. Tait is nearly all regenerative, all cash-pay and having massive impact in Tucson, Arizona.

Due to a minimal cash budget in the beginning, he did not want to reinvent the wheel and took a low-cost approach using grassroots, content and relationship marketing. He has learned to manage, motivate, delegate and convert prospects into patients without feeling like a salesman. Through this process, Dr. Tait has continued to grow and uplevel, and we are proud of him for how far he has come in achieving his practice vision.

We are also proud of all our other innovators, because we know first-hand how difficult it is when being 'outside the box'. We aspire for connection, acceptance and affirmations; without community, it is incredibly difficult to be an innovator in our world.

The Pressure Is Holding Strong - We Take It As Fuel

We don't believe that the healthcare crisis is going away. The pressure to do more and see more patients will not change. Many consumers are seeking better care and demanding better concierge medicine. The changes in healthcare are consumer-driven and we are at the start of a major shift. The opportunity is now to make a change in a booming, billions of dollars per year industry with an unrivaled unique selling position.

Those who win in the stock market see emerging trends and start taking action before it's too late. We hope that, inside this book, you'll be in that kind of leading position as you learn and implement the structure to freedom. You will find that, while it's up to you to create the income, impact and lifestyle you deserve, it can be easier than you think with guidance and support. This system, once implemented correctly, is providing consistent results and helping practice owners scale into seven figures of revenue (and beyond) in four years or less. This is possible even if you're just beginning your cash practice journey.

The goal of this book is to show you how to build a wildly successful practice, while changing the world modeling "The Five Pillars of Practice Success Platform." We have had to learn tough lessons in each pillar over the last nine years but were provided with great insight and wisdom due to some of those mistakes. We hope sharing our experience - including these 'unexpected outcomes -will help you be as successful as possible. We can tell you that doing the work in each one of the pillars is the only way to build a profitable, sustainable, scalable and impactful practice that will be fulfilling while giving you greater time freedom.

In the next chapter, we are going to cover the overview of The Five Pillars of Practice Success that has helped us replicate this model. Many physicians and practitioners tell me they are waiting to feel capable - "when I have more money", "when I get my book done", "when my job allows me", "when I can give up more clinic hours", etc. My answer to that is simple. If you are held back by any of those previous statements, your reason for why you are not where you want to be should be your reason why you need to start making changes now. Why should you miss out on this massive opportunity to redefine healthcare?

"Most people confuse wishing and wanting with pursuing. You must place your trust in action." - Price Pritchett, U2

CHAPTER 2: THE 5 PILLARS OVERVIEW

We are on a mission to redefine healthcare. We have invested millions into designing, implementing and refining this model and want to succeed with you, the visionary and independent thinker who is proactively choosing to create a medical practice that is focused on delivering remarkable outcomes. This is about building a practice that is dedicated to changing the lives of the patients and the community you serve.

Out of respect to our paid clients, we can only go so deep in this book. The purpose of this book is to share the structure, overview and critical information you can't afford to ignore if you desire cash practice success. If you are looking to go further after reading this book, this section reveals what we give each of our licensed affiliates and mastermind members to shortcut their path to success.

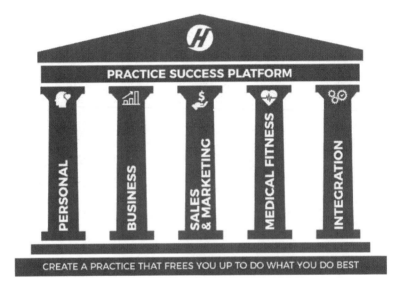

PILLAR ONE: **PERSONAL**

To fully experience the transformation you are looking for in your healthcare or wellness practice, we will start with the end in mind. That is, the outcome is you creating a practice that fills you at the core and allows you to do what you do best while having the freedom to practice how and when you want. Having a clear destination and knowing the exact steps to get there in the shortest time possible is essential. Creating systems and structure around your unique abilities, strengths and weaknesses will help you strategize the most rapid path to practice success.

Our mastermind members are given the confidence, resources and coaching to create their practice success blueprint, vision and specific action plan with your leading subsequent move so there is no guesswork on what takes priority. You will never have to think about what step is next; instead, you'll only have to implement the plan for accelerated success. A strategic plan is the greatest competitive advantage you can provide yourself and your practice. When you learn to lead from the front and communicate on a high level, you will have a high-performing team with a culture made up of strong communication, collaboration, accountability and execution.

During this pillar, personality and action-taking behavior will help you devise a plan that is customized so you can recruit, hire, onboard, develop and retain the right team based on your core values, unique ability, strengths and weaknesses. This allows you to have the right pieces for building a championship team for maximum practice success.

Personal Mindset Breakthrough Trainings are designed to overcome any fears regarding how to have difficult conversations, offering cash services, charging higher fees, or even talking about money effortlessly. They will also help you overcome your past and breakthrough your own physical addictions or mental blocks that prevent you from true success, happiness, fulfillment and joy.

Implementation Labs are designed to eliminate your insecurities and instill unwavering confidence in yourself, your leadership and your coaching. You will also learn time-saving productivity hacks to maximize focus, energy and implementation activities, allowing you to get more done in less time, giving you the work-life balance you deserve. When you do the personal and professional work, and your skills get stronger, you also gain emotional control and communicate at the highest level - that is when anything you desire can become possible. You can be the health hero and leave a legacy of great impact - all while having a joyful and prosperous life.

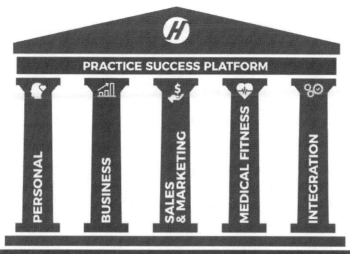

PILLAR TWO: **BUSINESS**

A scalable business is one that is able to create passive income, meaning without your time for dollars. If you are reading this, you already have the necessary skills to generate enough income to provide food and shelter for your family. The goal is to create a practice that gives you passive income that will allow you to continuously create impact and income while you are not physically working in your office. Organized systems, core processes and accurate data are key components to running a successful practice that can run without you.

Ask yourself, can your practice maintain productivity without a key team member? To scale and grow a practice that frees you up to do what you do best, you will need repeatable processes that allow each team member to operate at peak efficiency. The right team members in the right roles is essential for you to have personal freedom to practice how and when you desire.

In this Pillar, we teach and create a personnel playbook designed to help you attract, hire, develop, incentivize, retain and grow a championship team so your business can grow and scale to make more profits without relying solely on your time in the room.

Our entrepreneurial scorecard and key performance indicator (KPI) metrics dashboard are customized to measure immediately how your practice is performing. This will allow you to take all emotions out of running your practice, so you can make objective decisions, as well as measure - and manage - individual and team performance. The format allows for all team members to maintain focus on the important metrics, processes and action plans that ensure success.

Members are armed with our structured meeting format that eliminates micro-managing and difficult conversations while maximizing communication, accountability and execution on company goals. Most meetings lack the structure and next-step action plans to hold focus on the priorities that will drive the practice forward. Running high-performance meetings where everyone has a voice to identify and discuss practice barriers are necessary to achieve team buy-in and optimal communication in an integrated practice. After everyone is heard, the practice leader is asked to make a final decision and next-step plans are communicated. This is a critical step for achieving company goals and objectives.

Turnkey core processes, job descriptions, policy and procedure manuals as well as billing, coding and cash-pay pricing guides are established so you don't have to create anything or spend all your time reinventing the wheel. When your team is following our systemized and proven processes, you can focus your time on communicating your message, creating relationships and seeing patients.

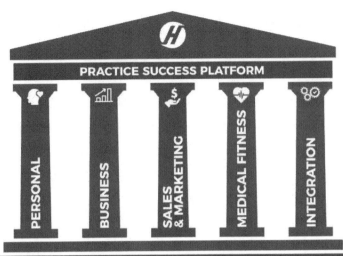

PRACTICE SUCCESS PLATFORM

PERSONAL · BUSINESS · SALES & MARKETING · MEDICAL FITNESS · INTEGRATION

CREATE A PRACTICE THAT FREES YOU UP TO DO WHAT YOU DO BEST

PILLAR THREE: **SALES & MARKETING**

Powerful patient attraction and sales systems are critical for you to help create the most impact! We will show you how to out-market and out-position your competitors to double - or even triple - your cash income in the next 12 months by building your brand and packaging your unique branded system that matches what your prospective patients are looking for in a healthcare solution.

After building your brand message and offer, we help systematize your marketing, so you never have to stress over where your next patient will come from for your practice. If you are like most medical professionals, you hate the idea of selling. We have our Selling Without Selling System that is loaded with educational content and messages that nurture and attract cash-paying patients who are seeking minimally-invasive alternatives to drugs and surgery.

In this Pillar, we teach our members how to develop a customized Practice Success Marketing Blueprint, Brand Guide and Marketing Calendar with metric-tracking worksheets so that they know how all their marketing and sales efforts are performing.

We allow our mastermind members to rebrand and implement our done-for-you marketing campaigns that have allowed us to see over 10,000 cash-paying patients in the last ten years. This way you can practice the medicine that will have the greatest benefit to your patients.

We teach you how to use our Selling Without Selling System, so you never have to talk about money with your patients yet have the ability to enroll them into your long-term treatment plans that will change their lives.

Our training resource guides will give your team the training to fully execute the four main marketing funnels.

This will also provide guidance to externally hire, implement and consistently execute your Marketing Blueprint and Calendar so you are not questioning what you need to do or who you can use to attract and convert patients.

We also use the power of patient testimonials and case study systems that allow your best patrons to become self-generating referral activists who can no longer allow you to be the best-kept secret in your area.

A properly executed message will create a deeper impact with the right prospects instead of diluting your message by trying to speak to everyone. This way you can invest more money in fewer places and see faster results (vs. spreading a little all over the place and seeing minimal results).

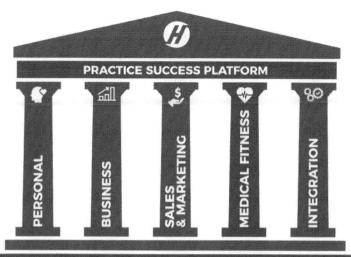

PRACTICE SUCCESS PLATFORM

PERSONAL | BUSINESS | SALES & MARKETING | MEDICAL FITNESS | INTEGRATION

CREATE A PRACTICE THAT FREES YOU UP TO DO WHAT YOU DO BEST

PILLAR FOUR: **MEDICAL FITNESS**

It's our belief that healthcare's absence of exercise, nutrition, and lifestyle modification as the first-line treatment is not healthcare - rather it's sick-care. Not only has our Medical Fitness Program been a great ancillary revenue generator, it has allowed us to provide leading patient outcomes while providing a major differentiator in growing our integrated cash practice.

In this Pillar, we'll teach, show and create how to successfully launch an online or offline ancillary revenue source that, in my opinion, has the most attainable marketing entry point. It has allowed us the ability to have a team that is on fire to show up to work each day, motivated and ambitious to work in a healthcare facility that is changing lives daily. It is a practice that is designed to be a solution to fixing the chronic disease and pain management crisis, so you can feel great about practicing medicine that is truly supporting wellness and transformational quality of life for your patients.

We provide our members with done-for-you educational PowerPoints, videos, and health and nutrition resources, such as our cookbooks and meal plans, as private label content for you to rebrand so you provide your patients with the life-changing tools they need in their regeneration journey.

By having a proven and marketable weight loss, fitness or health coaching program, you are able to consistently attract new and highly motivated patients within the practice. Adding a program of this nature will help you stay a step ahead of the competition by being the first in your area in the medical fitness market. Differentiation is, obviously, essential in a competitive marketplace. Even more, by offering next-level patient care, you are delivering on a new kind of patient experience - and that is a sustainable advantage.

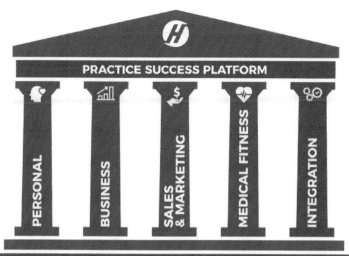

PILLAR FIVE: **INTEGRATION**

As a medical professional, if your practice model is seeing patients 1:1, there is a hard cap on both your income and impact in the world. I know you care deeply about changing as many lives as possible, but you also want to charge what you're worth. That's pretty much impossible without passive income.

The method we use to build passive income in our Integration Pillar focuses on building and automating your practice to produce income and outcomes without your time in the room. Whether it's having multiple providers, team members and / or systems providing self-service care, you are not required to be in the office to deliver patient value.

In this Pillar, we will teach, show and create how to prevent your integrated practices from operating in silos. We have created communication platforms and systems that allow a consistent, integrated patient experience so you retain patients, deliver a high level of perceived (and real) value and provide unmatched outcomes.

Our mastermind members spend time at our clinic in skill-building cadaver labs, shadowing and hands-on training in regenerative orthopedics, functional medicine/family practice, and medical fitness so they can see first-hand how each of our systems come together while avoiding the unnecessary temptation to reinvent the wheel.

Medical chart templates, treatment plans, patient infographics and communication tools are shared so you can educate and enroll patients into all the integrated services that allow for maximum profitability and evidence-based successful patient outcomes.

We provide our time-saving technology hacks that allow you to create systems that operate automatically so you can conduct an efficient and profitable clinic. Examples are an automated lead nurturing system that is effective for you at a fraction of the cost compared to having a dedicated person managing all your leads.

Our resource partner guide consists of all our vendors, contractors and suppliers at group discounted rates so you can immediately save time and money that can be better-spent towards marketing and hiring key team members (or simply add to your bottom line).

We have been right where you are and developed this platform based on our practical experience, so you don't have to spend years focused on figuring out how to create a successful practice or spend hundreds of thousands of dollars while struggling to achieve success. We have done it all and we're here to help you do the same without all the added work, time, mistakes or left turns.

Bonus Follow Up Quiz

It's time to pause and take The Five Pillars of Practice Success Assessment Quiz so you gain extreme clarity about your current strengths and obvious needs inside each Practice Pillar.

The quiz is here:

www.smartbizquiztribe.com/quiz/690

Oh – and you'll receive a complementary 1:1 personal session once we receive your assessment too!

CHAPTER 3: THE PERSONAL PILLAR

"A dream written down with a date becomes a <u>goal</u>. A goal broken down into steps becomes a <u>plan</u>! A plan backed by action becomes <u>reality.</u>" - Unknown

True to its' name, this pillar is where a lot of the personal heavy-lifting happens - which means getting down to the source of what sabotages what you want and how you have created results up until now. To show you just how far I had to come, I am - in an unparalleled way - going to share my personal story with you in this book. But first, here is the story of one of our innovators who, like you, knew there had to be more in her business.

In 2013, shortly after forming our new business, MedFit (designed to give practice owners the same medical fitness blueprint we used at Rejuv Medical to change the direction of healthcare), I went to a conference on Prolotherapy and PRP, where I met Dr. Tyna Moore, D.C., N.D. In the functional medicine space, she was becoming cold to demanding patients that require a lot of energy.

She did the technical work of running the practice and she was treating patients. In addition, she was grieving the loss of her mentor, Rick Marinelli, who had recently passed. He believed in her and motivated her to make a difference. She was ready for another quest. I knew I could help her see the true power she had by establishing why she went into medicine and providing clarity on the opportunity she had before her to create massive impact on her terms.

Since then, Dr. Moore has created her own regenerative medicine training foundation and mastermind and is no longer held back by industry egos. She has become a leader and a category of one in her naturopathic profession. She has relinquished treating patients who she no longer wants to treat and focuses only those who are willing to do the work. Dr. Tyna Moore does not accept 'victim' patients; instead, she accepts only those who are willing to take self-responsibility for their care.

She also formed her own mastermind as she no longer had the desire to see hundreds of patients each month. This year alone, she is responsible for helping over 15 female doctors have the starting foundation for long-term practice success. I am thrilled to watch her continue to step into her extensive abilities. Getting clear on her vision and purpose was the big stepping stone for Dr. Tyna Moore.

The Personal Pillar is what breeds life and culture into your organization. The Personal Pillar, shall you choose to accept it, has the power to provide joy and happiness.

Only once you're fully committed to the process of personal and professional growth can you best lead your team. This Pillar will set the path on the direction and work that needs to be done. When you make this a priority, you will show your team you're their fearless leader and worthy of following no matter the mountains that must be scaled.

I am going to share my three attainable superpowers to overcome every obstacle in your life. So you can turn pro, achieve a championship mindset, and reach your full potential in this incredible industry as a champion. Once you know these superpowers and how to use them, you're going to feel unstoppable as you start implementing them.

These superpowers allowed me to overcome low self-esteem, drug and alcohol addiction, saved my marriage and helped us build an $8 million integrated practice, as well as two other businesses ready to break the seven-figure mark. I know you can use them to change your life too - even my children use these three superhero powers.

The Bittersweet Blessing of 'Burgess Ears'

I grew up a happy kid with joy and extroverted enthusiasm. I was born with the 'Burgess ears' as my family calls them. It's a genetic feature that has been passed down for generations. I was teased by a couple older kids and consistently called Dumbo. I did not know any better and just figured they were bullies. All was normal until the fifth grade when I was in science class, and a teacher, who was not fond of my mother, stood me up on a desk and was talking about how my ears lacked cartilage. She explained that is why they would flop over as she flipped them, and all the classmates laughed. I was mortified.

I started acting out emotionally at home and became very depressed. My mother did not know how to help because I would hold it all in, then blow up verbally on her when I was frustrated or triggered.

After several outbursts, it finally came out why I was acting out. I didn't want to go back to school out of fear of being made fun of again, so my parents arranged for me to have plastic surgery to fix my ears. I had new and improved ears but the surgery had little success on my self-esteem -my confidence was shot. I became very self-conscious and introverted in every social situation except sports.

I discovered an extreme love for baseball, although playing any sport all day long was my only desire. It was my distraction and escape. When I was home or being told what to do, I would simply act out and lose control of my emotions. The depression and outbursts were extreme and, one day, after destroying several items in the house, I attempted suicide with a knife. My mother understood I needed more help than she could provide.

Due to the suicide attempt, I was hospitalized for two weeks on an adolescent mental health unit. I don't remember much of the experience except screaming at the top of my lungs the Michael Jackson song, "*Heal the World*." Thereafter, I was sent down south to Arkansas to live with my aunt and uncle. During the first day at my new school, I was teased by the kid behind me who was holding up a "Yankee" sign behind my head. When I turned around, he would quickly pull it down and the entire class would laugh. I turned around and punched him in the nose - and was promptly suspended for a week. I was not off to a good start at my new school.

My aunt was not tolerant of verbal outbursts, so I was locked in a small bedroom for the next three months. I was only allowed to come out to eat and go to school. I was miserable living with my aunt, so I learned to manage my emotions just enough to go back home where I had more freedom. And so, back home to Minnesota I went.

Sports continued to be my only escape and joy. In the seventh grade, I changed. I was bitter and angry with my father for being absent; I wanted him to be at home rather than traveling for his job. I began to live by my own rules.

My mother was a great parent and there for me, but I didn't listen to her. I hung out with an older crowd and started using drugs and alcohol to cover up and hide my depression. I would turn from shy and introverted into a fun party animal who would do wild and crazy things. As a seventh grader, I was hanging out with seniors. I became popular and continued to get better at sports. By the time high school came around, I was considered cool and popular with friends. However, I developed major issues with several figures of authority. I hated unnecessary rules and mean people and, to this day, unless a rule makes complete sense, I want to do the complete opposite. I am not sure the rebel in me will ever go away, but I have learned anytime I decide or desire to change, I can.

Sports were the only thing I did that allowed me to graduate. I dove in deep. I was not the most talented, but I outworked and out-hustled everyone. I focused on gaining every competitive edge and was nicknamed 'Charlie Hustle' because I had a motor that would not stop.

Unfortunately, in a small high school, there was one teacher for a singular subject from tenth through twelfth grade. I had major issues with the sternness, harsh demeanor and bitterness of this Social Studies and Science teacher. I did not hold back from speaking out on how I felt. And, as a result, I was kicked out of all my standard high school classes from tenth through twelfth grade. I was sent to a behavioral learning center in another town.

For all those classes, all we did was written video reports. I was okay with that as I knew I was going to go build water towers like my father, uncles and brothers. Even as a young kid, I loved making and saving money. Knowing I would make $125,000 or more per year - more than most college graduates - I always knew I would be financially set. The job was very high-risk, and I was the ultimate daredevil. Risky behavior was my second nature, so I thought I'd be happy building water towers. I had an '*I don't care, live life to the fullest*' attitude. By the time I graduated, ninth grade pre-algebra and part of tenth grade English was as far as I got in my education.

Bye Bye Play-Offs

At that point, the only reason for staying in high school was baseball. However, we lost in playoffs and I missed the game because, during the previous game to get to playoffs, I tore my meniscus for the third time.

We were a great team and were considered good enough to be able to compete for the state championship. I knew we had American Legion, which was summer league. We were off to a game at the start of playoffs and had just wrapped up practice. As we were walking off the field, one of my friends, who did not play, lit up a joint of pot. I took a hit but not to get high - I wanted to blow in my teammate's face just to be stupid and funny. The coach saw the act and I was immediately kicked off the team. They went on to win the state championship -this still lingers as my biggest mistake in life, and one of my only two regrets.

From there, I got very depressed. I drank a liter of vodka daily for the next 90+ days straight - I blacked out every night until I went to build water towers. Leaving home was probably what saved my life. Every day, I was making reckless decisions because I had no fear of or care about death. The water towers are where I learned very fast what real work and responsibility was for real. I had known how hard the work was, but now knowing that was what the rest of my life could end up being like was another story. What if I were to raise a family? I would not be present with my kids, as I would have to live on the road. I made ridiculous money for an 18-year old, but I had to turn to an adult quick as others' safety and lives were in my hands each day.

Building water towers is still a high-risk job today. Before I started, three of my uncles had fallen to their deaths while working on water towers. In the last 15 years, both my brothers have fallen and, luckily, have had no serious long-term damage. Seven years ago, my dad fell and broke his neck and is lucky to be able to walk. However, he is permanently disabled from most active daily living skills. As I write this book, just last week another gentleman was killed by a falling sheet of steel while, yet another broke his back - all in the same accident. My work ethic stems from 'anything is easy until you do water towers', which I did for four years combined. I built water towers one year before I went to college, two years after undergrad, and one year after graduate school.

That first year on the road was long. I missed my girlfriend, friends, partying and baseball. I was scared to go back to school because I had severe doubts as to whether I was smart enough. I may have gotten a D2 scholarship for baseball but could not get accepted at any four-year university. I had to take one year of pre-college credit classes at the community college before I was ready for generals.

When I came back, my best friend - who was still a senior - had the same teacher who had kicked me out of Social Studies. She told his mom not to let us hang out because I was a bad kid and would taint her son. I was so mad because I really was a good kid. I never forced anyone to party and accepted everyone for who they were without judgment. So, I could not grasp why this teacher would say such a thing about me.

But, at the same time, it was the greatest gift I ever received. My mind was made up at that moment in time that I was going to prove the naysayers wrong. All those who labeled me, I was going to show them I was a good, caring, kind and hardworking young man. I told myself I could put my mind to whatever I wanted and that I could make it happen.

All-In for the First Time

So, I went all-in with school and learning for the first time. Teachers were not telling me what to do. They did not care if I did not show up. And, thus, I thrived. I studied hard all week, played ball and worked my ass off so I could party hard on the weekends.

I was so pumped because, in my second year, I received Academic All-American status in baseball. For the first time, I gained confidence that I was intelligent. That if I could put my energy into school the same way I did with sports, I could be successful as long as I did what I was passionate about at the time. I already learned that talent and/or knowledge is not always the key to success. Rather, hard work and persistent practice at what you're passionate about wins almost every single time.

As I was wrapping up community college, I decided to go to St. Cloud State University because it was voted one of the top party colleges in the world and they had a sports management program. In addition, I had an offer to walk-on and play baseball. I thought that any job in the sports field would provide me a career in which I could be passionate. In the second practice, I tore my knee and had to have my fourth knee surgery. I missed three weeks of fall ball and missed the cut.

A friend of mine from another high school told me to try the D1 rugby club the university had - they were one of the top teams in the Midwest. I was a former football player, so I thought, why not? I ended up scoring in my first game and instantly fell in love.

I was still bothered by my past and was angry inside, but I found the physicality of rugby to be the greatest release in the world. I bottled all that anger and, when I was on the pitch, I wanted to destroy people. However, it was a healthy outlet, where my fierce reputation and scoring became applauded. I became a different animal on the pitch but was instantly a friend to all after the game. That was the beauty of rugby. It was a social sport and you even partied with the opponents after the game. I became very good. Rugby was my new addiction.

This is when I truly started to learn to deal with my past and my emotions in a positive manner. I started by forgiving my father for not being there through my difficult times, as he finally came to one of my college games. I stopped blaming teachers and mean or close-minded people for being the reason or somehow responsible for my reactions to difficult situations. Even though I still wanted to prove people wrong, I started learning not to speak my mind freely by swearing or telling people what I thought. Instead, I learned how to have strategic conversations while still being frustrated. Rugby became the greatest emotional release, and the foundation for a whole new level of communication skills.

I graduated Magna Cum Laude. My first year out of school I was a financial advisor. I learned a great deal about sales and investing but was too tempted by the monetary advantages the water towers provided. I built water towers for two more years before I was ready for grad school. I knew I had to have a graduate degree to get into the business offices of professional sports teams. This time, water towers were a strategic decision to save up the most money possible.

With my understanding of how to invest, I put away enough money to pay for grad school and I started investing in my future. The first week I went back to start grad school, I ruptured my right Achilles tendon. My rugby teammate, Nate, asked me to do one of my practicums at Gold's Gym where he was a sales associate. My practicum was over in two weeks when I was offered a sales position. I did sales for the first six months but fell in love with working out and helping others do the same. I decided I wanted to become a personal trainer.

Like anything else I found passion and love for, I dove in head-first and I went deep. That's about the time the show "*The Biggest Loser*" came out. I was hooked. I loved how the show utilized a medical approach to help those who were the most desperate. I was back to playing rugby again after a year-long rehab; my old minor injuries started turning into constant pain. I pushed through for the next year, but I was thinking I was going to have to give it up and just stick to amateur baseball and softball.

I met my wife-to-be, Kyla, earlier that year; we both finished grad school. I graduated with a 3.93 GPA. I had one A- that brought my grade point average down from a 4.0 the last semester. I was proud, but I beat myself up, like I did with anything when I didn't meet the expectations I set for myself. As Kyla and I were planning for marriage, the long-term financial outlook of personal training in a large corporate gym just did not provide us with the finances for the life we talked about living.

Together, we decided it was best for me to go back to building water towers for one to two years to pay for most of a nice house but, before I left, I wanted to go see Dr. Baumgartner for my second treatment. It was the show "*The Biggest Loser*" that spearheaded our conversations regarding how we could make a difference in the world.

The show proved how powerful a doctor's message can be when telling patients that it's imperative you focus on healthy lifestyle changes. Doctors are regarded as the highest authoritative source in society today. The unfortunate part is when doctors tell patients to eat healthy and exercise, they don't show patients the means or have systems to help patients make permanent lifestyle changes, nor do they have the time.

When I came home for our wedding on July 25th, 2009, I saw Dr. Baumgartner in the parking lot of Golds Gym. He invited me to join his practice. He told me I would be the key to making long-lasting lifestyle and health changes, and I would have several contact hours with each patient to help apply the healthy programs we created. And this is where it all began. I was a huge believer in his treatments, as by that time I had no pain and was excited to be back to rugby and all sports - pain-free.

One day, I asked my social media contacts for a medical fitness test drive. On Facebook, I stumbled upon an individual, Bedros Keuilian, who was promoting a product on how to attract training clients. After buying his digital program, we started receiving his automated emails. One email offered us an invitation to attend a weekend Fitness Business Summit 2010. As a result, Dr. Baumgartner and I were astounded on how little we knew about marketing.

What We Didn't Know Was Hurting Our Community

At the summit, I realized the possibility of what we could do. I thought, "*If this guy could do it in the fitness industry, why couldn't we model it in healthcare?*" I made a request to Dr. Baumgarten to register me for the Mastermind program, telling him he would not be disappointed, and I would do everything possible to implement the model and get a great return on his investment. He invested $14,000 for me to join this Mastermind group.

I quickly learned that selling blocks of sessions was outdated. I had no billing automation or marketing mediums for building the know, like and trust factor in prospects' minds. I was just advertising and promoting features of our program. I was doing one-to-one sessions and did not have large group training, and you could name just about any other operational detail - I had no clue about it. I started taking massive action.

We blew up when we ran our first low-barrier offer program. I learned how to integrate over half of the fitness clients into the clinic. I was impressed with how well it worked! I implemented everything that Bedros told me to do. Within eight months, we moved into a 6,000 square foot location.

At this point in my life, I was in a good financial position. I had a promising career and was happy in most all areas of my life. However, I still had several extreme behaviors in my life, despite several years of maturing.

Shortly into our marriage, Kyla and I started having serious marital problems. I worked like a madman and had a drinking problem. I didn't drink often but, when I did, I would blackout, nearly killing myself with the crazy stunts I would do while drinking or from the excessive amounts of alcohol I would consume. I was never mean or aggressive to her or anyone else, but I would do things that would embarrass my wife or not be able to move the whole next day due to the severe hangovers I experienced.

I still played sports five to six nights a week. When I came home from work, I would tune into ESPN and need to watch that for the next hour. Plus, I was working crazy hours. I grew up on the Iron Range and, in an environment where my family or water tower crews would swear every other word, I only knew how to argue with swearing and that was uncomfortable for my wife. I did not have faith in my life and that was very important to her.

But, because I love my wife and did not want to get a divorce, I said I would work on changing. However, this created resentment because, ultimately, I was the same person who she married, so I could not completely understand what I was supposed to change at the time. I still worked like crazy, but things did start to change.

In early 2011, I had another major rugby injury and had to have my fifth knee surgery. This was my most serious one yet. I only drank six times that year but, each time I did, I would black out, as I never learned how to have just one or two drinks. We gave up TV, which allowed me to be more productive and present with my wife when I came home. In that year, we also received our greatest blessing - Kyla was pregnant! I had told my wife that, as soon as we got pregnant, I would quit chewing tobacco, so I did.

Knowing faith was important to her in raising our family, I tried going to church with her. I attended several sermons and would stand up, sit down, over and over and nothing resonated. I felt judged and guilty afterwards for some reason, and I felt that all the church wanted was money. An old client of mine from Gold's Gym, Mike, and my co-worker, Carrie, went to another church and told me I had to go. I still don't know what happened because, for the first time, I didn't feel judged by the pastor as he admitted he was far from perfect. He was super cool, funny, real and the worship music touched my soul. I cried like a baby the first eight services.

Yet Another Wake-Up Call

The following year, I still drank a few times even though I had several amazing shifts in my life. Dr. Baumgartner and I were at a Mastermind conference in Las Vegas when I had another wake-up call.

I worked hard but continued to drink when I traveled due to my work hard, party hard mindset. Our first night there we had a great time, but I got drunk. I was enjoying the moment and doing my crazy, good drunk dance, but the next day I was sick, and Dr. Baumgartner thought I had alcohol poisoning. I missed the entire day of Mastermind, for which Dr. Baumgartner paid over $4,000 for us to attend. What an embarrassment!

That was the first time I understood just how serious my drinking was and that I could not handle it. Earlier that year, while on a cruise, I could have easily died. My drinking caused me to black out and, unknowingly, I ended up jumping into a lifeboat! Fortunately, I am still here to talk about it; sometimes you need to hit rock bottom before you're willing to change.

The next year I joined the 100K Information Product Mastermind run by Bedros Keuilian and Craig Ballantyne. After three years of learning how to market and run our fitness and practice properly, we joined this mastermind to bring forth our mission to change healthcare. We needed to figure out how to package and teach our program online, so we could start selling our MedFit licensed program to the world.

During the first session, Craig Ballantyne gave me a book called "*Turning Pro*" by Steven Pressfield. The premise is it's about giving up your amateur ways in exchange for professional behaviors. If you're looking to actually achieve whatever your dream is, you have to turn pro. Reading that book gave me clear examples on how I was living my life as an amateur.

I finished the book on the plane ride home and, over five and a half years ago, I had my last drink. Realizing if I could not hold my alcohol, I was not in full control of my life and destination. I was not going to be a major difference-maker in redefining healthcare as much as I thought I was and wanted without giving up my amateur ways.

That book and these two mentors have been life-changers for me. I no longer have any of the behaviors my wife wanted me to change, except for the fact that I have yet to give up sports. Ironically, at the beginning of July, just before starting to write this book, I ruptured my left Achilles tendon playing softball. It may be time to find other sports or means of competition that my body is more conditioned for if I am not able to come back 100%.

At times, I have missed drinking because of my introverted tendencies when I do not know people. Drinking gave me confidence to open up, sing, do karaoke and dance. Within the last year, I have danced again and sang karaoke twice. Little by little, all these things that I thought I needed drinking to be able to do, have become possible again. The greatest benefit of joining masterminds for me were receiving the tools to overcome mindset dysfunction. They provide the structure and community to grow myself and our practice.

My Growth Shows as A Rugby Coach

This provided me with closing the door on one of the last pains I carried from my past. In 2013, shortly after I quit drinking, I started coaching high school rugby. That season had the potential for a championship winning season. We had 17 kids; you need 15 kids to compete. After the first game, a parent caught four of the older players smoking pot in a car and informed me about it. The parent said he would understand however I chose to handle the situation.

My wife wanted me to cancel the season being that she is a school counselor but, despite this, I set a meeting at my house with the four kids. I asked them if they were willing to set up all the fields all season long, and I said they had to mentor some of the younger kids on the field.

I proceeded to mentor them about my past and how I made life more difficult for myself than it needed to be as a result of partying. I showed them all the wonderful possibilities for their future. They all had some sort of abuse and various addictions in their homes as well as difficulty listening to authority figures.

Later that year, we ended up winning the state championship. I knew what rugby did in my life and for others, so I didn't want them to lose something that changed my life in such a positive way and could be a great experience for them too. I felt completely redeemed and proud of what I had done in each of those kids' lives.

All four have turned into great young men; two are fathers of beautiful children, and good fathers at that. I felt God showed me he has plans that are more stunning than the original plan I had for myself, once I was willing to move forward in God's calling.

What I learned is none of this change would have been possible without the right support from my mentors, wife, kids, our team and for God's pursuit of me to let me know that I was called to do his great work. He provided me the strength to turn pro and showed me my ultimate dreams were within reach. However, it has not been easy. At times, I have wanted to quit and go back to drinking.

My Twin Mirrors: Sports and Speaking

When we started MedFit five years ago, it was hard for me to get on stage due to low self-esteem. From what I had gathered at that point in my life, I knew I could overcome anything I convinced myself to do. I realized speaking was just like sports.

Before every game, I would go to the bathroom three or four times and I would have butterflies in my stomach. But, once I started playing, all that disappeared. I was always confident on the field because I had practiced. I was prepared, and I was focused to win and play the best I could each game. I felt those same butterflies with each speaking opportunity, and usually for several days before each gig. Sports and speaking became one and the same for me.

Once I started speaking and the butterflies dissipated, I would speak with the same conviction that I played every game I ever participated in with fierce commitment to delivering my best and bringing value to the audience. Today, I'm doing it with ease and joy, shooting for the impact of reaching one person who will take action from the message. My videos and speaking engagements have provided me with some of the best connections of people opening up to me with encouragement that they, too, can turn pro and live the life they want.

I did not know these behaviors and sometimes extreme outlets were holding me back from my true purpose and potential. I am far better because I have overcome the majority of my destructive behaviors and know how to handle my emotions. I have come to realize God has blessed me with the strength to overcome and to fulfill my calling to change healthcare and be the best husband, father, friend and leader I can be.

At times, I still have a life of extreme behaviors, an impressive all-or-nothing mentality, and have several addictive tendencies but, when properly managed, they are also my greatest strengths.

There are times when I have a hard time finding middle ground, especially when things are stressful. I am still a work in progress. My recent Achilles rupture has proved to be one of the greatest blessings that I have had in life. I am finally going from thinking I need to be doing it all to being the best I can be in every moment. I have done the work and put in the hours to build a successful business. I was sacrificing my health and my time with my wife and kids. I was not the most present, as I hid from true connection. My family was secondary to the pursuit of changing healthcare. Now, for the first time, I feel my priorities are 100% in line with my calling and my ability to become the best human being possible.

I am still going to have to work to keep the complete joy and happiness I feel; however, I am happy to share that the joy I feel has come from the unmistakable messages my savior has shown me. As of now, I am no longer finding my identity in my work, but my identity in being who I was called to be here and now.

My True Competitive Edge, Values and Superpowers

I want you to know that any addiction or tough spot in your life can become your strength and will, eventually, have meaning in what you are called to do. I am now so thankful for everything that happened in my life. The teasing was necessary because it led me to sports, and sports are where I developed vision. Vision is my ultimate competitive edge for success. The work ethic I gained showed my talent, which is not a deciding factor for success as much as it is a persistent practice that is far more important. I am grateful for the empathic powers I gained from being teased. It became my unique ability to feel, connect with and lead others who are in pain and depressed. This skill turned me into a result-producing coach because I am able to help people work through their issues. Therefore, for me, in high school, when there was a kid getting teased, I would be compelled to help them. Being an empath is what gifted me the ability of knowing the people who I was led to support.

In fact, I have always been good at helping others release their pain but, at the same time, I did not let go of my own. Only recently, through therapy, I have learned that I drew up defense mechanisms. I developed amazing core values from my parents. From my dad, I learned the value of hard work and kindness. From my mom, I learned honesty and loyalty.

However, I also gained my own value of total self-responsibility for my life and my results. I came to understand that I had a do-it-all-on-my-own mentality. That kept me from releasing all addictions. They made it easy to hide and created a safety net for me to get a feeling of escape, so I could try to manage my emotions on my own or through physical sports. Just now I am learning to connect and share my pain, my problems and my emotions with my loved ones. I hid talking about my frustrations or experiences about my painful thoughts, even though I gravitated toward solving pain for others.

I am so thankful for my addictions because they have led me to helping others by having them turn to me and express their true feelings. They find comfort in me because I have no judgment as I have experienced most of what anyone else has encountered. I could meet them where they are as long as they had a desire for change. I fully accept who they are in their state of perfect imperfection. We work together on improving in steps that they choose are best for them after I help with providing structure. These conversations turned me into a great coach.

All I know is we all have a bigger calling and dreams that are bigger than our past and present problems. I do not want you to let your past get in the way of your dreams. We all have our sad stories and barriers we tell ourselves. You need to let go of past traumas or failures and let them be your reason to change and create a better life for you, your family and the people you serve. You can rewrite your story. You can lead and inspire your family, team and patients by becoming the best version of yourself.

Remember when I got kicked out of the playoffs? I got a second chance to become a coach. Just like with Rejuv, we could have kept our secrets, our challenges and our success all to ourselves. We are going to do for you what I did with those kids. We are going to teach though the hard lessons we have learned. We passionately and enthusiastically desire to coach you to have the same impact through your practice. We turned all our challenges around for the greater good. You were designed for massive results and, sometimes, it takes a community and coaching to experience that greatness. The world needs you-you are the frontline soldier. From all my life and work experiences, I have learned I have three superpowers: Determination, Vision and Turning Pro.

Living My First Superpower

I was always determined to succeed and win wherever I put my energy and passion. I had enough self-awareness to understand what I was good at versus what I was not. That gave me vision. I was always strategizing by looking ahead to figure out how to pull all the pieces together to execute and devise a plan to win. Combining vision and determination are what has made me believe anything is possible. It took mistakes, mentorship, self-reflection and profound change to realize I had to turn pro if I truly wanted to become my best me. I want to give you the formula of how to gain these three superpowers:

Passion + Purpose + Doing the Work = Determination

Determination is derived from doing what you are passionate about, finding the purpose for which you were given the skills to do, and completing the work it takes to achieve the goals you have set for yourself. Passion is usually easy for each of us to find at an earlier age. I am sure you are able to recognize a few of your passions.

Sports and adventure were my childhood passions. However, I was always working. At a young age, I was mowing lawns, shoveling snow and working any odd jobs to try and make money. Financial strategizing and savings were always passions of mine. Being an empath, I became a coach of helping others not just with pain, but also coaching my teammates to be in the best position for success based on all the factors of the game.

Looking back, I wanted to go to college to be a coach, or work as a business executive for a Minnesota professional sports team; however, I took my first professional job as a financial advisor. These passions were all present at a young age. Passion is part of the formula and, in my opinion, is essential for radical success and happiness in your career and life. But it's not enough on its own.

Those who find they are operating from passion will find it is much easier to go all-in. It makes it easy to want to learn, invest time and resources, and energy. Too much of anything can turn bad, even if it's your passion. For instance, I could play rugby forever, but my body is working against me. Therefore, by continuing to play, I am at far greater risk for a bad outcome at this point in my life. Yes, it could and would help me mentally but, if that is my only coping mechanism, then I'm using it as a cover-up. I could have stayed in a passionate relationship with an ex-girlfriend, but I knew she would not have been the mother that I wanted for my children. I knew someday I was going to have to turn any passionate relationship into a sustainable purpose, which meant finding a wife who would share the same philosophies in our raising our children. Then, as always, I was determined to succeed ever I put my energy and passion. I was always enthusiastic to strategize and put the pieces together to execute the plan to do whatever it takes to win.

Your purpose is inherent in your passion and calling in life. I will do anything for my family; I knew I always wanted one. After finding my faith, it was clear to me that my purpose was to help people get out of their pain and it piggy-backed perfectly with my passion to coach willing people to their success. Healthcare is where I have the greatest opportunity to help the most people. Purpose is what drives us to persist, even through the toughest times and challenges.

I would have failed without support and without my foundation in Christ. I knew I could judge my success on what I was willing to give up to get to the next level of success. To give up myself, my addictions and my coping safety nets knowing I am pleasing him has allowed me to overcome fear, addictions and misguided mindsets. This has led me to many of the changes that are necessary to fulfill my purpose.

To fulfill a purpose-driven life with such a significant goal - of redefining healthcare - means I have to scale large mountains. That requires passion and conviction of purpose to be able to have the persistence to do the work it takes for that level of achievement.

3 Types of Intelligence

The biggest mountain to overcome is usually yourself. There are three different ways of looking at intelligence: Adversity Intelligence Quotient (AQ), Intelligence Quotient (IQ), and Emotional Intelligence Quotient (EQ).

Adversity Intelligence Quotient is about your ability to continue to move forward through trying life challenges. When you're trying to go from building a seven or eight figure plus integrated practice, you're going to go through adversity. We have had turnover, loss of insurance contracts, new political leaders, failed opportunities and everything else you can name that most people face when running a business. We almost lost our building in the first year. I was losing my mind but, in the end, I still had to lead 50+ employees. It was not easy, but you would have had to kill me to stop me because I do not submit.

Going through tough times in life has taught me how to deal with adversity on all levels. AQ is like a muscle - the more weight you put on it without seriously injuring it, the stronger and larger it becomes - and I've needed it. The last few years, I have had multiple injuries as well as Lyme Disease that nearly defeated me, but I have done what it takes to stay ahead. I am going to fight harder than most people know how to fight. When you have passion, purpose, and you persist by doing what it takes, you will come out a champion.

To do what we have done at this point is a great success but, admittedly, the mental stress has taken a toll on my health and my family. It has brought me to a mercy point several times, but the strength of God has allowed me to manage and keep growing. I heard a quote a long time ago and I cannot remember who is responsible for it, "*If the task was easy and we accomplished it, it wouldn't have any meaning.*" In fact, right now as I write, I have the most I have ever had on my plate at one time. I am no longer concerned with any outcome. I am a survivor and, no matter what storm may come, I will resurface. There is no need for over-stressing anymore.

Not everybody wants to change the world. Many are fine with a modest impact, income and a simple life. Instead of scaling mountains, they want the green pasture and that's okay. The green pastures are beautiful and I believe it is noble to live with such simplicity. I commend anyone who has found peace and happiness in life, no matter what the circumstances or income they make as they do it. I do not want anyone to be misled. Creating massive impact or high income does not come with the green pastures very often. We have to be willing to work harder and learn how to strengthen our AQ. Embrace and welcome the storm because you will grow.

The next form of intelligence is your IQ. The <u>Intelligence Quotient</u> can be defined as a person's cognitive ability to learn. It is also associated with school performance, IQ logic, abstract thought, self-awareness, emotional knowledge, memory planning, creativity, and problem solving. Little did I know that intelligence comes down to your capacity to learn. It is hard to learn more without letting go of previous suffering or knowledge of information that no longer serves you. Not everything I have learned over the last nine years is my passion.

So, in order to open up to learning more, I had to say goodbye to a lot of my past and turn them into my greatest blessings, which left me open to learning and having continued growth. You have to say goodbye to all the pain and suffering of any circumstance. Unhealthy patterns are only in how people think. Suffering is separate from the painful experience itself and can be eliminated. For instance, when I was teased, I may have suffered pain back then or when I wiped out on my motorcycle and had road rash over 10 percent of my body, but that pain is no longer present. However, some people are still suffering from pains that happened many years ago. The only clear path you can take is to move forward in life. Unfortunately, no one can go back and erase bad past life experience(s) but we can learn, grow, and gain purpose from it all. And that is called radical acceptance.

Lastly, there's the <u>Emotional Intelligence Quotient</u> (EQ), which was tough for me. As you know, I would ignore communication when I was mad or frustrated and, eventually, just burst with the internal pressure expressing itself. People with high EQ are like the eye of the hurricane. There is drama and chaos all around, but the center of the hurricane is calm, predictable and consistent. In the past, my communication style was reactive. I made mistakes and still have the most room to grow in this area. In employee relationships, it is important to ask questions and not get defensive. The minute you point fingers or raise voices, walls go up and it becomes counterproductive to communicate further. Some people are passive-aggressive and avoid conflict at all costs which really does not work when solving problems together. If you want to have your best life and practice, cultivating your EQ is worthy of your time and attention.

Work Hard to Do Less

Nearly everything I have succeeded in to this point has stemmed from doing the work. I would be lying if I did not tell you that I worked hours that are three times more than most people. I have had to learn the hard way that it is not about the hours but the quality and discipline of your work. And that means doing more with less time by doing the things that matter the most. You can also work hard to do less. To me that is good; in fact, I am doing my best to make this happen right now.

Do not take that statement as a commitment for me to become lazy. Instead, interpret it to mean that I have to become a master influencer, developer of others, communicator, delegator, leader and manager. There is an art to maximizing time. I am still a believer in that hustle and grind are the easiest way to lay the foundation of success. (Remember, my nickname was Charlie Hustle!) If you do not learn airtight structure, have self-discipline and absolute focus, it is hard to scale the mountain and grow a big practice.

What I have learned about working hard and smart is structure equals freedom. You have to use your time on the items that move the needle. It is about using your undistracted magic to create your most meaningful work that is part of your unique ability. This is the time to focus on the most impactful next best moves, whether you have just 30 minutes or two hours. You need the discipline to not be distracted and get the stuff done that matters every day.

Shouts and Whispers

I get no less than one hour of my most important tasks done each day. My team hears me talk about the shouts and whispers; you have to focus on the shouts. Shouts are opportunities that drive the practice forward. In sports, a shout would be scoring. We need to score more points than the competition to win. In business, shouts are like focusing on marketing funnels, videos, sales conversions, relationships, developing others, system-building, writing a book and delivering successful patient outcomes.

Whispers are things like sourcing the cheapest medications, adding a new piece of equipment, doing taxes or bookkeeping, and considering which email operating system use. All are essential business pieces, but if you're not focusing on high-yield, say $500 / hour, tasks, it will be hard to make that income on a consistent basis. Everything that is not focused on "scoring" should be delegated (meaning, passed to another teammate in a non-scoring role). Those who score the most make the most. Teammates who know how to assist and put the scorers in the right position get paid well too.

Imperfect action has been the basis of our rapid growth. It does not need to be perfect, it just needs to get done. Knowledge is not power, action is. I know far too many info gatherers and people saying they will do this or that, and they never implement. You only get paid for finished work, so get stuff done. Take action and stop talking about what you should do. Do as an ant does - they carry up to 10 times their own body weight, are hard to kill, work as a team and are relentless in building a sustainable home for their community.

The Second Superpower

Seeing / Filling the Gap + Hyper-Awareness + Competitive Advantage + Staying a Step Ahead + Focus = Vision

The next step towards freedom, impact and income is vision. Vision is knowing what has to be done to achieve a desired outcome. Vision is seeing a gap and filling it, as well as being hyper-aware of each aspect of you, your team and your practice. Vision is fully understanding your competitive advantage, keeping you and your team intensely focused, and staying a step ahead of the competition.

Vision starts by seeing a gap in the market, my abilities, your team, and your patients. Being an empath helps me understand what people need. I can detect how others feel and pick up social cues at a high level. It's about seeing a need and providing various solutions that others may not be able to pick up on which creates a differentiating edge in business.

I have always made it a priority, in most situations, to provide value to any given scenario in which I was involved. In sports, I knew our gaps on my team. I wanted to win at everything I did; therefore, I studied our strengths and weaknesses, as well as the other teams we were playing. I warmed up early, so I could keep my eye on the other team. I knew who we had to hide or what adjustments we had to make as I watched for every competitive advantage we may have to strategize our future win.

Dr. Baumgartner and I knew there was a gap in the market. Many also saw the gap in healthcare. But the difference was that we not only have vision but are major action takers. We fail forward more often, but we quickly course-correct. We strategized plans to fill the gap, leading our community and now industry toward a brighter, more fulfilling, better future.

Now, many people just fail to start, do not do what it takes, or procrastinate too long so they can't see their vision through to the end. Amazingly to me, most people do not think on this level. For example, two years ago, we were at the Midwest championship rugby game. I barely practiced all year, but I was good enough that they allowed me to play.

As usual, I warmed up early and watched the other team warm up. I did light stretching and watched the other team fully run their plays. As soon as they blew the whistle for the game to begin, we went to the huddle and I said, "*You all need to get me the ball, there is no way the wing can cover me.*" Everybody looked at me like I was crazy. I hadn't been to any of the practices or games the past month. I had only played one game all season. My team expressed that we had better players than me at this time. They said, "*We have to run the plays towards the center position where James plays. He has been the star player* for the last couple seasons." I said, "*No! You guys have to skip the centers and get it out to me. Please trust me.*"

In the first two possessions, they skipped the inside and outside centers when we were in scoring position and passed it to me at the wing. I easily ran around the guy and scored our first two tries within the first ten minutes of the game. After that, they switched and put a fast guy on the edge and I was neutralized, but we already had done enough to win the game. That is one example of how to see, fill and use a gap to advantage.

Know the Gaps

What is your weakness? How do you hire around it? Do you know the gaps on your team? Do you have a strategic plan to fill it? What if you do not know your gaps? Who do you hire if you do know your gaps?

I knew my gaps in business were technology, administration tasks and networking. My first two hires were people who were much better than me in those areas. In fact, I am also terrible at spelling and grammar and, yet, this is my third book.

By the time you're reading this, you will see this is not a literary work of art, but it is a starting structure that I followed to get me to this point in two weekends. It will get cleaned up over time. I'm not saying it won't be good, but it is truly about imperfect action.

So, there is a gap in healthcare with too few cash practices. I know I have to act fast. The New York Times just published an article that made me sick to my stomach. Centers for Medicare and Medicaid Services is proposing paying all office visits the same, whether it's a level five visit or a quick five-minute follow-up. Robert Pear, writer of the article, "*Sniffles? Cancer? Under Medicare Plan, Payments for Office Visits Would Be Same for Both*" was published in *The New York Times*, 22 July 2018. This is not acceptable care, and profits over people has - once again - corrupted our healthcare system.

The next step of vision is the importance to be hyper-aware of your needs in each area. So, what are your needs for your practice? Are you cut out for management and a leadership role? If you are not willing to lead by example, have difficult conversations or manage expectations, you absolutely need somebody in a position that is focused on operations and production. If your operations are not efficient, it is likely you won't be very profitable and a sign you have a production gap. If you cannot provide a consistent or repeatable experience without a key person there, you have an operation or production gap. It is likely you have a marketing and sales gap if you do not consistently get new leads and new patients. If you are not booked out and have regular gaps in your schedule, you are going to struggle to make ends meet over the long haul. Are you able to leverage your technology to be better and faster?

You may only focus on what you've been comfortable with, or what your capacity has allowed you to do up until this point in time. But in all reality, you will need to know where you stack up in each area, and then put a plan around improving or you will never win the championship.

It starts with you being hyper-aware of your unique abilities, as well as your team's greatest competitive advantage. Jack Welch, legendary CEO says, "*If you don't have a competitive advantage, don't compete.*" He speaks of the 5% Rule. I know too many great, intense, well-intentioned physicians doing QuickBooks paperwork, spending time on administrative tasks and doing work that does not match the income they are hoping to generate (and which others can and should be doing).

If you are cleaning your office, or ordering supplies, and you are not seeing the income you want, you have a mismatch of using your competitive advantage to your best level. I am not saying if you enjoy mowing the lawn or doing the dishes that you're a failure! But, if you are choosing to perform these mundane tasks vs. helping more patients, creating content, managing or growing your business, you are not leading in your full capacity. 95 percent of the tasks that don't move the needle should be delegated to someone else, so you can focus on your 5 percent competitive advantage. If you absolutely love some of these tasks and they are a mental break for you, that is different. But make sure you analyze the opportunity cost before doing more of them again.

Reverse-Engineering to Go Forward Faster

I understand each of my unique abilities in addition to my three superpowers; these are where I work to spend 95 percent or more of my time executing. I am a sponge. My capacity to learn and implement fast in a area that I have passion for is remarkably strong. I can hear a keynote speaker and, if it is impactful, I could repeat it in the training to our team and clients.

My AQ is that I easily overcome adversity and I just keep going - when things get tough or overwhelming, I do not let anxiety or stress slow me down or lose emotional control any longer. I say to myself that nothing is the end of the world and remember that I have been through worse. I am a strategist, so I can see the gaps and then fill those gaps.

I attack problems and find solutions that move us forward in the quickest manner possible. I am good at leading, developing others, coaching, creating content, confident in action, selling, influencing and now becoming confident in speaking. What it all really means is I solve problems, manage, motivate, delegate, create and sell on a high level.

How do you start to understand and learn who to keep around you and understand where gaps can be filled? What is going to keep you one step ahead? How do you know the next best action you and your team need to take? Knowing who you need to add to your team and strategic planning is staying one step ahead. It is great when you have a medical assistant who is always two steps ahead of you.

Having a professional who does the thinking for you versus one you have to continue to direct is worth their weight in gold. Some owners and managers keep that employee forever. Many great managers stay a step ahead because they know they have hired people who can stay one step ahead of them. Too many hire friends, family or people like them. I knew where I was weak and built a team around me that would keep us moving forward.

Kolbe is an assessment that will show how you and your team are inclined to take action. For instance, I am a Quick Start - that is my primary focus. I can make good decisions when I have just the right amount of information. However, on big contracts and significant corporate decisions, I want somebody who is more of a Fact Finder to gather the necessary data. And I absolutely need a Follow Through personality with me. I am fast to delegate, lead my team to the next action steps, and bring new ideas to the table. But I need somebody to finish and manage tasks to make sure they get completed.

Accordingly, I have an amazing executive assistant and she does all my scheduling, travel accommodations, follow-ups, keeps me organized, and sets time in my calendar to help me follow through on all the things that need my attention. Having the action takers around you who operate differently than you can help you stay ahead, move at a faster speed, while minimizing mistakes and rework.

Strategic planning and goal setting around your vision is a critical step that will allow your team to visualize the plan and have confidence that they are taking the right actions when they can see the big picture. It is very difficult to be taking the right action steps every day unless you have an intensely focused plan. It is essential and leads to stronger communication in execution that is not operated in silos.

To stay ahead, you have to reverse-engineer your end goals and provide a roadmap for achieving it. There are numerous statistics on the advantages of a strategic plan with goal setting at each step of the journey.

We need to start with the end in mind. What is the impact, income and lifestyle you want? We help our mastermind members set realistic goals based of their vision. This is important because most overestimate what they can do in one year but severely underestimate what they can do in three years with a focused and strategic plan. What do you want your practice focused on in the next 14 days, 90 days,

1 year, 5 years, and even 10 years? Do you have a daily action plan?

For us, we move three steps forward and, in some circumstances, two steps back. In terms of our growth, five steps forward, and one step back. However, there has always been progress. I keep my eye on where we are going and how we are going to get there. When I look at our past strategic plans, even now at times, I have not been happy because I wanted to be at 200 locations by now. But

I stay grounded because I am able to see the progression when I look at our plans. I have had to learn to train my mind to not be frustrated for not being where I would like to be right now. Instead, over the last year, I have learned to fall in love with the process and celebrate small wins along the way to inspire my team. This allows me to be happy in the process as well.

How do you break down a strategic plan that is focused? One way is to ask the stakeholders and participations in it.

So, in our case, I ask all the regenerative injection physicians: how many regenerative cases do you want for each month? For example, they want to go from an average of two stem cell cases a month to ten. It would be a great one-year goal to go from two to ten per month. However, most are not thinking about step one.

Once we set that year plan, then we are able to break into 90-day windows and pick four company initiatives in each quarter of the following year that would lead us to hitting that goal. The first quarter, for instance, might be to create three marketing funnels: a regenerative lead-quiz, an info packet and a seminar funnel. That would be a great task that would drive leads.

The next quarter, we decide to hire and train someone who can convert those generated leads, follow up with existing patients and schedule patients.

The third quarter, we fix the landing page and build autoresponders to follow up with leads who did not convert, and the team builds the sales talk for the seminars.

The fourth quarter, we start running ads and seminars and monitor all our conversions and key performance metrics.

All these actions would lead to a general build of more patients each month and, when well executed, should lead to hitting ten new stem cell cases a month by the years' end. Goals without specific action steps from start to finish will typically have far less success than if you have a detailed roadmap to get you to your destination.

The next step is for you to know more about yourself, so you can start assessing what you need. Here are some self-assessment homework assignments.

1) Take The Five Pillars of Practice Success Quiz (www.smartbizquiztribe.com/quiz/690) to find the gaps in your practice you need to fill.

2) Have yourself and some of your key team members take the Kolbe test.

3) Administer the Myers-Briggs Type Indicator test, which is a personality inventory and will show you how you and your staff members work with others, allowing you to have better interpersonal relationships.

4) I recommend you ask some truth tellers about how they perceive you and your practice. These people are not your

mom or your close friends, as they typically tell you what you want to hear. No, these people who are willing to tell you exactly what you're asking regarding how people perceive you.

5) Take the *Think and Grow Rich* assessment by Napoleon Hill. Learn about how you perceive money, how you become more successful and develop a better relationship with money.

6) Brendon Burchard's *High Performance Habits* assessment will help you understand the necessary behaviors to perform at the highest level and give you a plan to become a high-performer.

For me, this assessment was a real eye-opener. I have even made immediate changes after taking this assessment and am able to see where I can improve my energy and productivity. Even though I thought I was highly productive, I desire to be more productive, so I can work less hours. My slowing of production stems from my assessment of improving my energy. This year, I am building action plans centered around taking care of myself first by exercising, reading and meditating, which are all the self-care habits I did not feel I had time for during the last two years as we had our biggest growth spurt.

Where do you stack up? Do the homework and embrace where you are and have self-love. One of the biggest breakthroughs I've ever had was two years ago when I was starting on my journey to restoring joy in all areas of my life. I was at Mike Koenigs' Speak & Profit event.

At this event, you had two attempts and I was good on my first run but had lots of feedback for improvement. I took the feedback, adjusted my talk and, over the next day and a half, I practiced continuously. I spoke for the second time and nailed all but one part.

My first reaction was 'I messed up.' I was unhappy with my performance because I had done better in the previous practice runs. Mike said, "*Wow! You're way too hard on yourself.*" I said "*Yes, but I have very high expectations for myself and I'm committed to getting better. I practice and work hard to improve.*" He said, "*Well, it looks painful and stressful, what do you know about yourself? Do you grow?*" I said, "*Yes.*" He said, "*Do you practice?*" I said, "*Yes.*" He said, "*Do you get better at everything that you commit to?*"

I said, "*Yes!*" "*So then stop this negative pressure you put on yourself and start measuring your progress!*"

My mindset immediately changed. I started developing a love for the process and the gradual and quantifiable progress. I no longer beat myself up - I just measure my progression. If I am lacking progress, I simply ask myself if I am doing the work necessary to improve. If I am doing the work, I know I will naturally get better in time.

Therefore, I have let go of the comparison of other platform speakers ahead of me and instead I say, "*I, too, will be there in time.*" Knowing that if I am committed, and I do the work, I am - without a doubt - going to grow.

After your self-assessment, decide what to outsource or hire around your weaknesses and gaps. Continue to focus on your competitive advantage and your strengths. As I mentioned earlier, one of my weaknesses is spelling and grammar. Learning how to communicate and write more effectively is important; therefore, I continue to work on that weakness because if I do not grow here, I cannot be as effective as I need. I choose to work on this weakness because I understand the importance, but I will still outsource to someone who has a strength in this area to clean it up. Also, becoming an excellent communicator is an area that I feel is very important for all of us to grow in to have influence and authority in redefining healthcare.

Regardless, you must maximize your strengths and unique abilities to get to your 5 percent but grow your weaknesses if they are getting in the way of your success. If you are not communicating or managing at a high level, you need to grow in this area, outsource or hire someone who can communicate, develop, lead and manage. Continue to reevaluate as time passes. There is a good and bad way to view each gap and weakness. View all the areas strategically to determine where to improve - or not. You are only as strong as your weakest link. You cannot be weak in marketing and sales, operations or your personal areas; if you are, you cannot sustain your business and grow.

The Third Superpower

Serving + Giving Up Amateur Ways = Turning Pro

Now that you understand vision, the last superpower is Turning Pro. Turning Pro to me is about becoming the leader you can and want to be. It is about trading in your amateur ways and giving back by serving a greater purpose than yourself. If you remember, my earlier motivations were to prove how incorrect those who wrongly labeled me as an adolescent teen and young adult really were which was a great motivator, but it only took me so far. It started to shift when I knew God had laid a calling on me to be the best leader, husband and father. My purpose was not to prove people wrong, but to truly change lives and serve a greater cause. I was self-serving by trying to prove the teachers wrong, even though it felt good.

To truly have the most freedom, joy and impact, one needs to serve a greater purpose than oneself. You have to give first, without expectations. We need to have a "give, give, ask" philosophy; we give, meaning you can't have a scarcity mindset. We have grown on all levels because we do what we can to help others without having an ulterior motive. *The Go Giver* by Bob Burg is one of my all-time favorite books. If you lack in this area, it is where I would recommend starting. When you become a giver, you become worthy of being followed.

We have our core values and mission statement hung on our walls. Our three core values for Rejuv: Virtuous, Brilliant and Results. If we are not in the business of serving others and being true to our core values, it is hard to have a team follow us. Being virtuous entails the belief that everybody is equal and makes a difference in our model. We work together despite personal differences for the shared satisfaction of making an impact.

Brilliant involves us always growing and changing. If this is truly our passion and the career we are supposed to be in, we will naturally grow, but we need to be willing to put in the work and continue our education.

Our last core value being Results (driven) because, if we do not deliver results, we do not sustain. For example, if a personal trainer cannot transform their clients' lives after training and development, this may not be the best long-term position for themselves or their company. Or as a front desk representative, if people's needs are not efficiently met and they do not have a favorable experience, this person may not be in the right position. We have to ensure we properly train and evaluate each position to see if our team members are in the right seat. We desire driven people who are innovative in executing new possibilities to create health and wealth, which means you need to have a team who can and will do great things and *that* is about serving beyond oneself.

The next thing is you have to give up your amateur ways and not just be a giver, but a leader and a master communicator. As I have shared previously I did not always have the highest EQ (<u>Emotional Intelligence Quotient</u>). A Pro has high EQ and is strategic, calm and collected. If you want to have the best life, your ability to communicate at the highest level is the best skill you can attain. In order for you to grow in your practice, you need to be willing to go outside your comfort zone one step at a time. It doesn't have to be huge steps, but you have to grow because your income will not surpass your self-worth.

Every system - including yourself - is perfectly designed for the results it produces. Therefore, if you change nothing and expect a different result, you may end up frustrated and disappointed.

For change to occur, you or the system needs to adjust - and frequently. This means you must abandon criticism, past failures, overcome adversity and just grow. Your purpose is waiting for you to have the courage to step into it through growth.

I have had to level-up in every way - and it tears you at your core to become an excellent husband, father, leader and world-changer. To start to scale larger mountains, you must learn to become a visionary leader - it's not an easy road. I push forward with determination and purpose. These are the same skills I teach to my kids over and over and over again. We have a saying in our family, "*I'm a Burgess! I am, I can, and I will.*" We grow that way.

The Bigger the Dream, The More Important the Team

Our success at Rejuv is because of our team. The bigger the dream, the more important it is to have the right team. They are the ones who do the work, follow and support the mission. We are much stronger as a team than we could ever be alone. Your team is the direct line to how well you are able to scale, grow and sustain a championship caliber team you can take anywhere. But your vision, core values and leadership determine how you get there; you create the vision and positively influence people to follow.

Even when the storm comes, and it *will* come, your success starts with you and having a championship mindset. The victim blames the team saying, "*It was my employees' fault, my partner is holding us back, or these patients don't have the money for cash-pay services.*" The champion is the leader on the team, encouraging everyone to do their best and driving a culture of excellence. Are you ready to learn how to Turn Pro and be the championship-style leader?

Less than half of most company's employees know their organization's mission statement and core values. Therefore, you need to make them truly living and breathing representations. Nearly two-thirds of employees say their company does not have a strong work culture. In this case, it is on you to establish the culture and set the stage for your current and future workforce. You need to establish a culture of growth by holding your core values, which means if you do not follow them, nobody else will either.

Five Attributes of a Leader

There are five attributes of a leader. The first attribute is self-driven leadership, meaning s/he should not have to be told what to do. If you have to constantly repeat over and over again to do something, that person is definitely the wrong individual to lead your organization.

Secondly, it is going to be difficult to acquire followers if you do not have enthusiasm. Like I said, I am not the most extroverted guy but, when you find me in my right passion and area of interest, I am full of enthusiasm and passion. Third, a leader must generate results. If I cannot get results in what I am doing, people will have a hard time following me and the business will suffer.

The fourth attribute is decisiveness. Leaders have to be decisive in order to move forward. It's hard to scale and grow your practice without making fast decisions. You can always course-correct if you make a wrong decision but being indecisive as a leader makes it hard for your employees to follow you.

Lastly, leaders have higher expectations of themselves than they have of their team. Team members are not listening to your words - they are watching your actions. So, are you on time? Are you focused and dialed in? Are you communicating? Are you maintaining structure?

The Pro leader is doing the work with the team, but the amateur leader will say, "*Do as I say, not as I do.*" If I haven't shown the team I can enroll 20 consecutive people in a row with cash-pay services, it would be hard to hold them to any kind of similar standard. Leaders must lead action. They are not info gathers - they implement what they learn. Leaders do not chase hundreds of shiny objects but, rather, we make sure something is good and working effectively before we can move on to the next task. We form habits that increase our capacity and our output. We complete our work and celebrate imperfect actions and successes.

When you are a Pro, you will have to be comfortable with being a black sheep. A Pro is not influenced by smaller minds. It can be a lonely road and a road less traveled. Your circle of influence will matter, but be aware of your friends, family members and your partner, as they can be a major reason for being held back. I am not saying you have to get rid of them but learning how to appropriately communicate with them is important. If you do not get rid of the cancer and drama, it will hold you back.

Next-Level Community for Next-Level Support

I strongly value the community that I center myself around. The one thing I have grown to love about being different from everybody else is that I am wired differently. I talk a lot with my mastermind friends about how grateful I am; although I paid to hang out with a lot of them, I stopped feeling like a loser because they, too, felt just like me. They are all obsessed with building their practices.

You have to surround yourself with like-minded people who model success. You have probably heard the phrase, "*If you're the smartest person in the room, you're in the wrong room.*" Being competitive, I was open to other's successes, but driven to come back to show I could do the same. I did not have to create most of the business systems we implemented. We modeled after other successful owners; being around big thinkers and visionaries is critical to your success as most people are green pasture thinkers versus Mount Everest climbers. I am pushed and propelled to greatness each time I am around next-level people.

Therefore, being in a community where we are walking the same path with next-level people, especially if you do not have a lot of support at home and at work, is critical. The alternative is doing it on your own.

According to Jim Rohn, "*You are the average of the five people you spend the most time with.*" I believe this is true because you tend to think and pick traits from the five people that you spend the most time with and align with their thought process. Your thoughts control the outcome.

Success and failure are the thoughts that occupy your mind and the people you are surrounded with every day. Those thoughts become your daily actions. The actions become the fixed habits, and your habits become your belief system. Your belief system determines your outcome. That is why I strongly encourage you to join masterminds and get coaching. You are changing and not everyone else is going to but, remember, you drive the culture of your practice.

More than half my speaking gigs have come from people I have been in masterminds with over the years. Many of my partnerships have derived from masterminds too. Much of my growth has developed from learning new things, then competing against the members to implement what I have learned. I am a competitor, meaning, I want to go back to our business and implement and have the same success my mentors have had in their businesses.

To sum this up, Pros model, learn, implement and do the work. I have never quite understood why people go to conferences and are critical of people who are having massive impact. Those who are critics and consistently talk negatively about others are usually not successful themselves; therefore, I will model success. Pros invest in themselves, because we know we are our own greatest asset. Pros pay for speed, and don't reinvent the wheel. Pros understand that sales and marketing are the driving force of a successful, sustainable, scalable and profitable practice.

Permission to Go Bigger

I want to let you know you are on the right track if you are reading this book. You should stop the worrying, enjoy life, have positive impact and make money. The worst-case scenario as a medical professional is if you lost everything. But you should be able to start back up and learn from your mistakes. Remain connected to your source and stay the course - you are your most valuable asset.

I want to give you permission to play a bigger game. The trait I admire the most about Dr. Baumgartner is his faith. He has no fear when it comes to taking risks in business. There is no room for fear in risk-taking and visionary thinking. He knows if it all went away today, he has attained the skills to make himself successful no matter what. Most people think it is when they have the capabilities, when they have the money, when they have the new location, when they finish school, they will be ok. But to create massive impact and wealth, it's not about that; instead, it starts with your commitment to taking action - today.

Once you commit, you gain courage when you step outside your comfort zone. You also learn you are capable of amazing things. If somebody else has done it, you can do it too. With practice, your capabilities grow. Confidence comes when you are prepared and when you are focused. Just like in my public speaking, once I was capable of it, I started becoming confident. Please remember, we never have to peak - we can always be climbing, growing, soaring.

There is a secret sauce to all of this. When you enroll your patients into life-changing treatment programs, you're increasing the ability for both of you to have a better life. Being successful starts with you being a good student. How can you ask your patients to invest in themselves by paying for cash services if you are not willing to invest in yourself? Growing is showing your brilliance. I know you are well on your journey to Turning Pro or you wouldn't have made it this far in this book. Just know it all starts with you and your ability to uplevel - it's what we are all here to do.

In conclusion, determination is doing the work you were called to do. Vision is knowing what has to be done to achieve the desired outcome. Turning Pro is leading and acting because growth only comes from change. To sum up your new superpowers: Determination is about doing and Turning Pro is about becoming your best self to see your Vision through to being reality.

CHAPTER 4: THE BUSINESS PILLAR

"Winning is not a sometime thing; it's an all the time thing. You don't win once in a while, you don't do things right once in a while, you do them right all the time. Winning is habit. Unfortunately, so is losing." - Vince Lombardi

When I met Dr. A., she was frustrated because she was not able to grow her practice. She did not want to add any more patient hours, but she did not understand how to make more income when she was maxed out with her hours.

After my initial conversations with her, I asked what her assistant was doing. She said, *"Whatever I asked him to do. He operates the front desk and checks patients in. The other is doing the billing."* I responded with, *"Do you know at what level they are supposed to do it at? Do you have any expectations or benchmarks? What would happen if that key person left?"*

Dr. A. was flabbergasted by all these questions and felt a little bit uncomfortable and embarrassed. I said, *"Don't worry, you have spent thousands of hours learning your medical skills and are capable of learning anything. Not all of you were trained to understand business, marketing and sales. In practice, you have grown successfully, Dr. A., because you care about patients and you get good outcomes. That has grown your referrals. Your ability to scale and grow will come when you fill some of these key gaps in running a proper business system."*

Interesting enough, shortly after our conversation, Dr. A. terminated the two employees and, just one month later, was having greater success. Her employees were only answering the phones, scheduling and doing basic administrative tasks. It was obvious they were not in the business of helping her grow or improve office efficiency, by any stretch. But she had lacked a measurement system to see how they were performing. When we got clear on their duties, determined the expectations and put processes in place, we found out rather quickly that they were good people who were simply in the wrong positions.

The Business Pillar focuses on core processes and performance metrics of your entire operation. Systems need to be designed for operational efficiency for patients and team members. Team members are trained to run the systems that have been put in place. All processes and positions are documented and reviewed for operational efficiency, consistency and high performance. For example, if someone leaves the company or is out for any reason, the business can run without a key person.

Automation is used where repeatable information and processes can be released without human touch points to enhance speed and repeat without detracting from the patient experience. One example is automatic billing. Another example is email autoresponders, which is used to deliver important information that helps patients better understand their care and allows us to consistently follow up without unnecessarily using our teams' resources. We have an obligation to ensure that our systems and processes are efficient and repeatable, that they have been tested to work, reduce waste and can be reproduced consistently by our team members.

To start the journey, the first step in the business system is defining your core processes. We have identified seven core processes: human resources (HR), marketing, sales, patient experience delivery, financial, compliance and legal.

For the purposes of this book, I am going to dive a little deeper on the HR processes because this is where some practice leaders who are running cash practices need the most work in order to make their practice successful. I believe the Business Pillar is the foundation that determines whether you have a sustainable practice that can run without a key person. You either have a job or a business, and a business should be able to be sold and leave you with wealth at the end of your time. We are here to create the foundation of lasting success, so you can have the impact, income and freedom that you desire.

Creating a practice that is consistent, predictable and measurable in terms of performance gives you the data and foresight to determine your next best strategic growth moves. Additionally, creating an accountable team with high expectations while incentivizing top performers is crucial. As mentioned previously, the bigger the dream, the stronger the team must to be to make it happen.

All About Human Resources

The Human Resources process includes: recruitment, job descriptions, employment agreement, expectations, growth plan, onboarding, accountability chart, employee development process, retention, process manuals, job checklist, time management calendar, compliance training, policies and employee handbooks.

The first part of the HR process is recruitment. We are not posting for a job opening - we are seeking candidates for a career opportunity. You need to change the phrasing from job opening for a receptionist to career opportunity. To post our positions, we utilize social media, careerplug and recruiters to make sure we reach our goal and are always looking for the top talent. Only 33 percent of companies ask employees to share company news actively or share on their social media sites. In other words, you can get top talent by just being resourceful. It is not always about needing money to scale and grow but can be about using the resources you have wisely.

When we do interviews, it can be incredibly time-consuming and costly without a strategy to eliminate extra time and work. Starting with a simple five-minute pre-screen, you can verify the wage ranges are a match, job duties and requirements are aligned, hours and schedule requirements match up, and ensure time periods of previous employment are clear. Verifying these aspects in advance will help eliminate well over half your candidates instead of wasting time interviewing the wrong people.

The next step is an in-person interview. Make sure each candidate is asked the same questions, so you do not get legal complaints down the road for discriminatory practices. Our third step is a shadow experience. There are different rules and regulations regarding this, so make sure to check your state laws. The shadow experience has helped us ensure the culture matches for both parties. This step has helped lead us to understanding the people who would not be a good fit. At the end of the day, this three-step process has helped us recruit much better candidates and find team members that end up sticking around. On average, it takes 52 days to fill an open position. So, for positions that are important, we always keep it a pre-screening process to find the right fit for high-demand positions. One of the costliest mistakes in practice is having the wrong hire or high-turnover.

Job descriptions are the next section of HR systems. We are clear on having job descriptions that have all the job duties, main responsibilities and job expectations, while reviewing the accountability chart that shows their direct supervisor and main responsibilities of the position. Every hired employee finalizes by signing their job description and employee agreement to acknowledge all responsibilities and ability to meet the demands of the position. The benefits package and merit opportunities are also described in detail, as well as acknowledged and signed for before work begins.

Once we start employment, everybody has an orientation, along with onboarding and systematic training, and a job development process. We put great emphasis on developing and evaluating each team member in the first 90 days. We do comprehensive check-ins at 30 days, 60 days, and a full evaluation right before 90 days to determine whether the candidate is the right person in the right seat.

During the check-ins we cover four areas that must be a match. We fully review the core values, job description, key performance metrics and then have a conversation about the one thing that will make their life easier and the one thing the supervisor believes will help the team member have a long and successful career at Rejuv. If they are falling short in any of those areas, we create and communicate a developmental plan at 30, 60 and 90 days. If they end up being the wrong fit, we have to make an appropriate decision before 90 days. We also continue check-ins as needed and perform a comprehensive annual evaluation.

Many of our mastermind members need direction on the "one thing" conversation. Maybe the employee has been found to talk too much and prevents others from accomplishing their roles to their highest capacity. It is possible they wear perfume that bothers co-workers around them. You have to be able to say the one thing that you are really enjoying about them in their position, and the one thing that could use change that would help them fit into the team better. Our evaluation process uses a consistent template that is used in all evaluations, so we are objective and not subjective in our findings. We must invest in accountability and make sure we are all in complete alignment. If people are under-performing, getting written up, and not hitting the marks of their job, we must do the hardest part of running a practice and let good people go. (Of course, this also means they are being called to doing something else that is a better fit for them, but that's another discussion.)

The key is in documenting every circumstance that is not aligned with the company's values or when people get performance warnings. Our first step of discipline is a verbal warning. Even when a verbal warning is given, we follow up with an email thanking them for the meeting and documenting the importance of what was discussed. If the behavior is repeated a second time and any time thereafter, we have a formal written warning. I cannot stress enough the importance of documentation to avoid paying unemployment and potential legal ramifications.

At the end of the day, we have to develop and analyze our people. On the flip side, we invest in our team's continuing education. We send our team to mastermind conferences, but we have them document what was learned as well as their ensuing ideas to be presented to our team. The development and continuing education is only useful if implemented. We have to develop by teaching and observing whether they are able to implement the training they've received.

For example, if I am teaching a salesperson who struggles to achieve a greater than 50 percent closing rate and they do not implement the training provided, that is a problem. If they had an alternative solution that was closing at or above benchmark metrics, I would not have an issue if it was done differently as long as it provided excellent patient care. We must commit to accountability and have high expectations if we are going to be a high-performing team. We also have to make the decision when people are not able to perform at a high level to let them go so they can find another opportunity where they can thrive. This is the hardest decision and probably still the most challenging aspect of leadership that I have had to grow into as a practice owner and leader. I fully understand our success is based on the team that we have; our team is a greatest asset.

Therefore, we have implemented a detailed termination process. We also commit to a retention process that allows us to be recognized as a top place in our community to have a long-term and successful career. One report suggests 75 percent of workers voluntarily left their job and did so due to their bosses, not the position itself. People do not quit jobs - they quit bosses. That is why you need leadership, development and accountability. It is also why you have to develop a level of loyalty where they know that, if the business is growing, they can grow with it.

Not everybody has the resources to invest thousands of dollars to pay for top talent. That is why we have creative benefits that help staff feel cared for and appreciated.

Small perks like eating out, gift cards, appreciation awards, affirmations, culture-building activities and community involvement are all key components to employee satisfaction. To retain people, we get creative with benefits such as: health insurance, Aflac, paid time off (PTO), free medical services, free gym access and anything that can help them experience our offerings.

We put forth a constant effort on educating our staff, especially in our integrated model. At times, you will hear practice leaders saying their people tell them they are too busy. Therefore, they over-hire, and when they over-hire, it is really important to have job checklists and efficient time management training in place. Every operational process has been mapped and timed. It's important to know how much time an assignment takes to complete. If people are finding it difficult to complete all their responsibilities, they are asked to bring issues to meetings to talk about different solutions to resolve the issue. All members are able to brainstorm so if somebody is not able to keep up, we do need to have a solution to help the team member. If you have solid accountability and metrics to prove efficiency, you can determine whether the role has grown too much or if you have a performance issue.

In the beginning, we grew our clinic too fast. Our first few years, we experienced inconsistent HR problems, and it nearly killed our company at one point. For example, one person wanted the same time off as another. We were flexible for the people who asked for more and we quickly learned the ones who did not ask would become very frustrated. That is when we created fair and consistent policies. Our employee handbook addresses all our policies and we make sure we stick to it unless it is a very unique circumstance. On a personal level, I would always be willing to help somebody out, give a loan or do a favor but, within work, it must be consistent effort for everyone. That entails the dress codes, paid time off, raises - you name it, there needs to be a consistent policy in place for all team members.

Another critical core process that determines cash practice success is your marketing and sales core process. How do we track success? We track all the important metrics. We have marketing and sales scorecards on the departmental level, as well as individual key performance metrics. It's critical we know the cost per lead. Then we need to know our conversion rates. At our seminars, we understand the percentage that converts into new patient evaluations. We track new patient evaluations to conversions to treatment plans. We know the average reimbursement per referral and average lifetime value per patient. For our sales staff, it is really important to know our set, show and close rates so we can reverse-engineer our numbers to determine the necessary call volumes.

There is no guessing on how we hit the monthly sales target. I would know my salesperson needs to make 500 calls a month to hit their 30 new patients per month goal.

When you have these numbers, you can start to fully predict your entire financial outlook. We keep accountability to the objective numbers in our practice. We do this because it's difficult to manage what you cannot measure. Therefore, we must help our team focus on the items that move the needle.

We use a method called Traction Entrepreneurial Operating System to communicate and execute to vision. We have complete clarity and focus on 90-day windows to work on the things that lead to our year-end goals. The number one goal of our financial process is to increase revenue, increase the lifetime value of the patient and reduce expenses. We have a top-level scorecard, meaning now I only work from the office two days a week and I travel the rest of the time. Therefore, I need a top-level scorecard so if I am out for three weeks and the revenue is down, I should be able to see our total leads and overall conversions based off total new appointments to determine what is happening. Our scorecard should tell the story of what is off-track when we are not performing at the goals we set.

Then beyond that, there are departmental scorecards that include our revenue cycle, physical therapy department, fitness department, clinical department and supplement department. Each team member has individual key performance metrics and, when done right, the individual numbers add up to meet the departmental goals, and the departmental goals add up to meet the company scorecard goals at the top level. Hence, this is our financial process.

For the clinic and gym processes, everything is mapped from the 'Tell, Show, Teach' model. This model entails us telling people how to do it by documenting it first, then we show them by demonstrating for them and going through the process, then next we have them show us by them going through it. During this, we sit over their shoulder and coach them as they go through the process. Finally, we have them teach it to us without us or another co-worker saying anything to determine whether they understand the process.

Another core process is the compliance and legal process. Our compliance process consists of HIPAA, OSHA, Stark, anti-kickback, blood borne pathogen, sexual harassment, corporate law, HR law, training and documentation requirements. I recommend you purchase a compliance program and have an attorney on retainer like we have done once you get to a size of 25 employees or greater. Prior to this, you still cannot ignore these programs, but you can typically keep up with the work demand or outsource before you grow past this point.

If you want to err on the side of caution, start from day one. It is very important to keep current with workers' compensation and unemployment laws in your state. We love staying on the leading-edge and being innovative, but I recommend legal support before acting where you are unsure. The potential ramifications of being set up wrong is too great of a burden to carry. One always wants to have the right checks and balances; therefore, your compliance processes, legal processes and business systems are part of your foundation for sustainability.

Our last core process is communication. We always make it a priority to have our team fully understand our vision, and how we are going to get there. Our team knows our yearly goals, our 90-day windows and our weekly objectives. We communicate these through various ways. We utilize our SharePoint system that has company communications and our document library. We use emails broken down by departments and have an 'All Rejuv' subgroup.

Communication was the biggest challenge while we were growing at an accelerated rate. Keeping everybody up-to-date with communication can be a challenge because not everybody is fully engaged at all times. However, we have everybody in weekly departmental meetings using an organized meeting format. With this system, when we implement traction, there is no hiding from accountability and not getting things done because we set tasks for who is doing what. We discuss issues and we solve problems. We assign to-do's based off of what was decided and we keep the team moving forward.

CHAPTER 5: THE MARKETING & SALES PILLAR

"Because the purpose of business is to create a customer, the business enterprise has two—and only two—basic functions: marketing and innovation. Marketing and innovation produce results; all the rest are costs. Marketing is the distinguishing, unique function of the business." – Peter Drucker

Dr. M. entered our mastermind and was making $100,000 per year. He was frustrated that he was not able to grow to a respectable income like many of his peers yet wanted to practice medicine he felt great about with his patients. He desired a cash-pay clinic where he could provide regenerative therapies. He was living paycheck to paycheck due to his loan and house payments.

I asked him what he was doing for marketing. He said the group he was in did not have a marketing budget for him. He was asking his patients to be his referral system. After a coaching call, we determined he was not providing any value for his market to get to know, like and trust him. The only marketing the clinic was doing was purely promotional and was only describing the services offered.

Prospects did not know the difference between what he was doing versus what everyone else was doing. That was the first lesson I taught him. People do not buy better - they buy different, because everybody says they are the best. How you communicate your message is the difference-maker.

Dr. M. has turned into a content- and value-providing machine. His message is out there. He went from being in a practice of making $100k to opening his new practice and being confident in getting new patients. In less than six months, he went from not making money to having freedom and independence, as well as attracting new patients. He is just at the tip of the iceberg in his new practice journey.

A common pattern of disconnect I see is that many medical practices and business owners are trying to be everything to everyone. When you do this, it is difficult to create an emotional connection and response to the prospects you are trying to attract. When you cast a net that is too large, your message becomes diluted and your connection suffers. Marketing and selling is really about learning how and who to market to while delivering a message that shows you can solve their biggest problem.

The next level is learning how to create one piece of content and leveraging your time to get it on multiple platforms. When I do one video, I want that to go to five places. We drive content to multiple funnels to create community omnipresence. Then when you get these leads, it is teaching physicians to sell without selling, and then converting prospects into long-term programs that actually change their lives.

We are going to focus this chapter on patient attraction, conversion systems and strategies that are working right now. I would like you to think of marketing and sales as the roof of your building; if your roof leaks, you will never have security because your business will be a wet, leaky mess.

If you do not know when your next paycheck is coming, you cannot take time off, you can barely make ends meet, and you have a job but you do not have the freedom that is possible for you. If this is the case, then you need to get a patient attraction and conversion system that works great for you.

The Riches Are in The Niches

It begins with understanding your target market of ideal prospective patients. Too many people choose way too large of a market versus picking a specific niche market. What are your niches' demographics? Is it females age 30 to 55 with an average household income of $80K plus, like we targeted for our local fitness program? What are their psychographics? What are their behaviors? How do they think? How do they feel? What are their thoughts? Where do they hang out? What do they do? What keeps them up at night? Once you figure out your market, you now have to start talking about what your message will be that has direct relevance and appeal.

What is it that you want to be known for? We believe we have the top non-surgical and medical fitness integrated clinics in the world. Therefore, it is our obligation to market and connect with those who are in need and searching for such solutions. What is that one piece that puts you out in front that makes you unique from everybody? The thing that makes people think of you as the go-to person? It should be the service you love to deliver. The thing that you cannot not talk about... it gives you energy and enthusiasm to do more of it. It makes you sizzle and shine and gives people immediate openings to want to work with you. This is called the throughline to everything you offer.

My throughline, originally, was medical fitness. It was pure passion for me. However, I realized that was step four in the process of changing healthcare. With our model, people needed to have the right vision to personally grow while having the right business, patient attraction and conversion systems in place before they could add medical fitness. They needed to have an already successful practice before adding another ancillary revenue source that was not in the providers' direct control.

We initially believed everybody could have the same success we did but, when we look back, it was because Dr. Baumgartner was already full, and I worked like most people are not willing to - every day. He already had a profitable practice before I joined him. Now my purpose is helping practice owners run a very successful practice, so they can add medical fitness and join the mission to help redefine healthcare. That is why we have changed our business name from MedFit to Healthovators. My throughline is now Cash Practice Success.

A throughline also means it is your entry point. It does not mean you do not offer other services, treatments or procedures but, in order to stand out in a sea of competition, it's a great idea to become the go-to expert in one area. Next, you uplevel people into another level of service that continues to add value to their lives.

Know and Tell Your Unique Brand Story

The next step is to create a brand story and unique branded process. When we start telling our story of why we do what we do and what that means for them, we can start to connect with our prospects. People do not just buy on facts and logic - they want an emotional connection and some sort of proof your system works.

The greatest brands and companies have an emotional connection and a great story. They make you feel like Apple or Patagonia do. You experience something internally and you begin to feel like you are part of the brand and what they stand for as a company.

When we started MedFit, I did not know how to tell my story and, when I did, it did not have the substance that proved value and, therefore, did not create repeatable success to my market. I never had an issue with attracting patients for transformation because my story was relatable and helped them on some level.

Learning how to market and communicate through email marketing and Facebook led people to me because I knew their pains or their standpoint of how they were feeling and I could communicate through cultivating relationship and then provide solutions to what they were seeking. These people learned what I stood for, what I was good at, and that I was humble, had flaws and that I was weak in several areas just like them - and I showed social proof I could get results. Therefore, learning how to tell your story and your message, while being able to inspire confidence in your program through your unique branded system, is key to your marketing message.

With our clinic, we educate about our unique branded system called Regenerative Healthcare. A system that restores and regenerates health without drugs or surgery. When people go through our entire process, we believe we can provide consistent and predictable outcomes. Our promise is we can help transform those who suffer from disease and degeneration while looking to avoid surgery and cover-up medicines. Again, no one else at this current time has the same identical offerings or message that we do. What makes you stand out will be key and a necessary message differentiator.

When you deliver content or have the opportunity to speak to your prospects, you will need to be able to relate to the target group as an understanding member, not as a foreign diplomat. Unfortunately, when many doctors try to market, speak or use social media, they lose people with science. We are not trying to educate other doctors but rather to inspire and speak at your prospect's level and incite their transformational desire. Once you know and understand everything about your prospect, you can create the most effective marketing campaigns.

Strategy, Strategy, Strategy

Before you start burning up your cash for marketing efforts that may or may not be effective, it is imperative that you plan your marketing strategy. The first thing that should be listed in your plan is the type and size of your niche, as well as the marketing vehicles you will use to capture your niche.

Once you have defined your niche market, it is vital to formulate a marketing plan. Too often when I start working with practices, many have never taken the time to get their marketing dialed in. Before we hired a team of experts, each Sunday night I would ask myself three very important questions as follows.

1) What am I actively doing to get more patients each week?

2) What is our secret to getting them results, then turning them into long-term patients and raving fans who tell all those in their circle of influence? Yes, I do want our patients to not need us for acute or chronic conditions if we provide great care; however, all of us can benefit from long-term prevention and health optimization.

It is important to know the difference between a one-time patient and a long-term patient. A one-time patient is someone who bought from you one time or as a short-term solution. A long-term patient is someone under your care and protection. It is a relationship that goes beyond a single transaction. Most practices I start with have no idea of the lifecycle of a patient, the average visits per referral, and average monetary value per patient, which will make it very difficult to understand what to spend to attract new patients.

3) What value can I add to my circle of influence, patients, team, family, friends, community and affiliates? We must get results or add value to the people with whom we are in relationships. I call this relationship marketing, which is far more effective, affordable and is how you build a tribe of raving fans who refer their circle of influences to you. It is why we are where we are today (and much less about how well or how much we have spent in marketing initiatives).

After you understand these three concepts, you can dive into formulating your plan. But without the preceding, your attempts will fall short of the potential value and benefit you can add to society. If your product or service adds value, you are doing the public a disservice by not learning how to market ethically and effectively.

7 Factors to Setting Up Your Marketing Plan

There are seven key factors to setting up your marketing plan successfully as follows.

1) Find, define and dominate your niche. Typically, successful practice owners view themselves as a specialist and not a generalist. Niche yourself down. Become the expert. Go narrow and deep with a mindset to dominate!

2) Figure out what your UBS (Unique Branded System) is; why you instead of someone else? Think about all the alternatives that people have for medical services in your community. Why should they choose you and not your competitor? What makes you unique, different and better? How can you communicate that message in your marketing that is a derivative of the transformation you are providing? We call this, "what is in it for them," and not what you offer. What visuals or infographics can you create so your process makes sense to your team, patients and prospects?

3) Become the local celebrity and face of your practice by telling YOUR story. Everyone has a story and your story is unique to you. Most physicians do not tell their personal story and reason for doing what they do. The personal story should be relatable and is what will attract and allow people to connect with your mission

more than any other marketing factor. Facts tell, stories sell.

4) Systematize everything! Have a step-by-step process so that your business can run without you being there. The most successful practices have owners or team members who work on the business and not just in it. This is the only way you can create time, freedom and replicate how you provide services. Your plan must be well documented, communicated and practiced by all.

5) Utilize Facebook, YouTube, Snapchat, Instagram, Twitter, email and your website to market your practice differently than everyone else. Provide videos multiple times a week and give your community a "peek" into the operations, the community that you have built, share your insights and the patient transformations that you've delivered. Too many medical professionals are complaining about people getting rich in the online medical industry and pushing out what they consider bad solutions, meanwhile they themselves are producing zero content. Almost as bad, they are communicating content that only appeals to other medical professionals and not the actual prospective patients. Blasting great content on today's social

media/online space is the fastest way to build the KNOW, LIKE and TRUST factor.

6) Once you drive traffic and leads to your website, it must be able to communicate your transformation, as well as educate, entertain, provide social proof and, ultimately, capture people who visit so you can start nurturing the leads. Too many people give up after a lead is contacted one time or after the first visit but, if you stay in front of people with great content, you will meet their needs when the time is right for them. You need a system to follow up both digitally through retargeting your custom audience with email automation and on the phone for maximum success. No, I am not talking about calling people if they tell you to stop. I am talking about caring more than they do at the present moment in time until they are ready to commit to change.

7) Culture + community + results = the "magic" potion of your business. And the "magic" potion is what leads to patients becoming raving fans who are referral-giving machines. Your job is to make your patients and team evangelical about your product and service so that they tell everyone about you! This does not happen

overnight but can be executed with the right long-term strategy.

3 Factors Before Investing in Marketing

Here are three factors to have in place before investing in your marketing plan:

1) How much should you spend on marketing?
This depends if you are already established or just beginning your business. Your advertising budget should fall somewhere between 3% to 9% of your gross revenue. In my first years of starting the fitness side of the practice, the budget was around 15%. We lacked any formal marketing plan. I was throwing out tons of money, not tracking returns and was still waiting for prospects to come through the door. Even though we were able to gain some traffic, we over-spent in many areas.

2) How are you going to track your return on investment?
At a minimum, you should get a 2-to-1 return on investment on all your marketing dollars. Today I require nearly a 3-to-1 or greater ratio on our paid marketing to continue the ad spend. If it is short of this return, I know something needs to be changed, such as the message, the

headline, the landing page, the offer or the advertising medium. For this reason, it is important to test and track your results. You can test two separate direct mail pieces to a small sample of your target market and see what piece gets you the most leads. You can use two different phone numbers to track the results. You can also use two different Facebook ads to the same program to see which one generates better results. This is called A/B testing.

3) What will you do with the leads when you get them?
Marketing is just one piece of the advanced picture when it comes to getting new patients. Simply put, marketing attracts leads to your business and to express interest. For many practices, they can generate leads, but the next step is what to do with those leads once you receive them. Unfortunately, too many critical leads get lost in the mix and there is very little, if any, follow up. If this is the case, you are lacking a lead nurturing system that provides massive value and education. It takes on average, 8 to 10 impressions before people are ready to take the next step.

Once you have done all the above, having multiple marketing funnels will spread your message and may connect with someone who may not have received it in another medium. Personally, I may be a great prospect for a company, but I would never find their ad in a newspaper or on television because I do not read the news or watch TV. The prospect might hear a radio ad, see you in the newspaper or have a friend who uses your service, but it was the direct mail piece that got them in the door. That is called the 'force multipliers' of marketing. For this reason, it is difficult to get a 100% accurate result in tracking one medium, but all your messages can be used together to leverage your results. In my experience, it will be one message that finally brings the prospect to you. If you're not tracking or testing, it is imperative that you start now if you would like to make the most of your marketing investments.

Most practices and businesses will run newspaper ads, print flyers, pay per click campaigns, radio spots and create websites - and that all costs loads of money. Some completely fail to get a 2-to-1 return on investment in these high-cost mediums. This is exactly how we started.

Another mistake practice owners make is by not investing more when they are getting a return. If I stick two dollars in an ATM machine and four dollars comes out, I would keep pumping money into it. I am going back to that ATM repeatedly. But you need to know WHICH ATM it is that is giving you that return; hence, tracking your marketing results data.

Before you start shelling out money, you must first start with the free and most effective methods for creating likeability and trust. Many successful individuals I have spoken with feel that traditional marketing has passed its time and the key for most local practices is relationship (content) and digital marketing. Our focus has dramatically changed to any medium that allows us to provide content and connect with our prospects.

Basically, content marketing is the art of communicating with your customers and prospects without selling. It is non-intrusive marketing. Instead of pitching and hard-selling your products or services, you are delivering information that makes your prospect more intelligent. The essence of this content strategy is the belief that, if we as businesses are delivering consistent, ongoing and valuable information to prospects, they will ultimately reward us with their business and loyalty.

Many consumers have simply shut off the traditional world of marketing. We still advertise on the radio, but only as the medical and fitness expert on radio stations, or with celebrity endorsements that have had great results with our regenerative services. On the show, we provide value by offering advice on how to make healthy changes, and talk about fears, desires, hope, myths and our story. We then close by inviting (leading) them to our website.

To stand out in today's saturated business landscape, most of your marketing dollars should be spent while building a relationship with your community and current patient base. This type of marketing will lead you to be the go-to source in your region.

For the last eight years, we have invested over $275,000 in mastermind programs to learn to dial in our marketing, systems, communication, message, management and leadership skills. These have been the best financial decisions we could have made and have yielded exponential returns. Without the help and guidance of successful business owners themselves, it would have taken many years of financial struggle, along with intense trial and error. I am not sure we would have survived through our trying years without the support and systems we have received from each coach and consultant we worked with through the years.

One big a-ha moment for us was when we realized that we were just selling features of our program and not the transformation we help create, which benefits the person, and is the real story behind our care. Our ads would have information such as: "*We provide metabolic testing*," "*The program is medically supervised by a doctor*," "*We offer grocery shopping tours, cooking classes, bio-identical hormones and regenerative procedures.*" Blech. Boring.

As we mentioned earlier in the chapter, you cannot be everything to everyone without a defined storyboard. Remembering this one rule will leave a meaningful impression and set the necessary tone: any marketing or content piece must state the transformation offer your service or product provides to your patients.

Several practices spend an astronomical amount of money on fancy websites that have a generous amount of information and look pretty. That is great but, typically, they are not successful because they are not pushing emotional hot buttons. They do not have a strong headline, an irresistible offer or social proof, and they fail to call the prospect to action through solving the prospect's first problems with a free gift of some kind to capture the lead.

Once we have the prospective patient's information (email and first name), we can start providing ongoing value through education and nurturing sequences. It is great that you can help everyone, that you have three degrees, provide six different programs, and you have the best equipment and, logically, you do need all that, but the reality is that people are seeking you for a pain they want solved - not for all the other "stuff".

The 9 Elements of Direct Response Marketing

When we market, we are looking for a direct response to the offer or action suggested. This type of marketing is called "direct response marketing." With the nine elements below, the prospective patient is led to a clearly defined action.

1) **The headline** - You must capture the attention of the audience.

2) **Story with agitation** - This is speaking the issues and problems your prospect has through using your ideal patient's words.

3) An irresistible offer - This is what a prospect will get for taking action with your practice.

4) The science or reason behind your irresistible offer - If it's too good to be true, they won't believe it. You need to substantiate your irresistible offer to make it real.

5) Your UBS (Unique Branded System) – Our proprietary examples are: Regenerative Healthcare System to restore and regenerate health without drugs or surgery. The Five Pillars of Practice Success Platform, The Medical Fitness I.M.P.A.C.T. Plan — essentially, something that separates you from all the rest, and shows your prospect you have an organized system for producing outcomes and the desired transformation.

6) Social proof - The greater testimonials and case studies you have, the better. The next level is learning how to handle your prospects' main objections through your patients' stories. All the people who went through your program almost did not join for one reason or another, so it is important you ask them to state their fears and concerns prior to committing. Answer the mental questions they're not asking by sharing patient successes and experiences.

7) Create scarcity or urgency that leads the prospect to immediate action - This is a true statement that should create compelling urgency to take action right away. For instance, we reserve a handful of spots prior to one of Dr. Baumgartner's seminars. If there are 20 people in the room, we state we only have room to help start some of them before the seminar ends.

8) The bullet points of benefits and likely transformation they will get from your offer - People don't like to be sold but they do like the idea of predictable transformation - for which price becomes no object. Clearly state what your potential patient will receive by taking advantage of the irresistible offer - today.

9) A strong call to action with clear directions on what you want the prospect to do next – Whether it be to go to your web page, call to sign up for a seminar, schedule a consultation, have an office visit or experience trial period, you must tell them what to do next.

Making Your Marketing Efforts Work

There are multiple types of marketing and advertising mediums that we could put our focus on - it's a big world out there. Whether it is paid or free marketing and advertising, you need a few high-performing funnels to best reach your target market. Each medium can bring you more leads and prospects. More leads equal more patients when you have your back-end automation in place. Each one of your mediums must have purpose and be strategically used and measured to determine effectiveness. Focus on relationship and content marketing digitally before investing in traditional and paid advertising mediums.

Many businesses start investing all their efforts in paid advertisements before researching the overlooked, more important, more effective and much more affordable relationship and content marketing strategies. This is because every advertiser you sit in front of will tell you how their medium is perfect for you and that you will miss out if you do not take advantage of their service. Advertising is also done for you and requires no work, an advantage that you pay for with premium rates.

Print marketers pray you will just hand over money and accept the first idea they come up with so they can move on to finding more business. They also hope you do not track your efforts because they can make practical sense of your dollars instead of using true data. They will make claims that your competitors are there and that it works great. If you are not achieving an impressive return, they will tell you it takes time and you should add to your frequency.

As your practice grows, I ask you to consider hiring an in-house marketing and sales manager to spend all their efforts on tracking, making compelling copies, creating new business, growing community relationships and maximizing free content marketing opportunities before paying for more outside advertising. The goal is to create as many force multipliers as possible. We do this by having several effective marketing funnels all working to get our marketing message to our target market.

Grassroots marketing takes work but it's by far the most important of all the marketing strategies to build your relationship in the community. It is easy to have digital ads or have the newspaper and radio craft you an ad and you are done. Not only will that probably be the least effective, it is also the most expensive. You must do the free stuff and that involves getting out in the community including, but not limited to, speaking, writing and video content every chance you get, along with social media, joint ventures, chamber meetings, referral generation systems and transformation contests.

The online marketing and paid tools can be extremely effective as well, but I have seen many owners and managers get too comfortable sitting behind the computer. Mediums like Facebook, YouTube, Instagram, Search Engine Optimization (SEO), Pay Per Click, email marketing and having an effective website are significant to your success. The key is finding models that will work for you. Take the time to make a system or follow ours so you are not running around doing everything half-heartedly. You need to combine both online and offline, free and paid advertising, and pump money into the things that work well for you at building trusting relationships. This is the long-term approach that needs time and resources invested into it to make it work.

Now I will give you the why, what and how to convert the formula, allowing you to have the impact, income and lifestyle you deserve. The question that I ask people is, "*Do you have a deep desire to transform health and happiness?*" Most fully agree with that they went into practice to help people. I ask people, is money good or bad? The answer is it is neither. In the right hands, it is great. In the wrong hands, it can be bad. Is persuasion good or bad? It is neither. Bad, if you're a lunatic like David Koresh leading people to their death. Good, if it's being used to change the world. Great, if it helps your patients take action towards an outcome they desired, and your program has the potential to change their lives.

Over eight years ago, I learned a hard lesson on the importance of persuasion and influence. Jen walked into our fitness center looking to lose weight - she was about 150 pounds overweight. When we first started, I was selling individual sessions versus long-term transformation programs. I had her committed to ten personal training sessions. In those ten sessions, she lost 20 pounds, which was a great outcome in a short time. Then she told me she could do it on her own. I knew she had gambled, drank and had all these other habits, but I did not fight for her to continue to replace those spending habits on ones that would change her life.

I got a phone call six months later that Jen had died of a stroke. I took it really hard personally because, if I would have known then what I know now, I believe she would still be here today. I now consider that with every person I come in contact with and call that my 'mom factor'. I treat each patient as if it were my mom walking into our practice. My mom has lupus, heart disease and chronic pain. We grew up living a very unhealthy lifestyle but, luckily, we were very active. My mom is very unhealthy and if she came into our practice with a desire to change, I would want her to utilize our entire health system. I would ask her to work three days a week with the trainer and health coach. I'd also want her in physical therapy, as well as taking multiple lab tests and being on all the right nutraceuticals. I want her treated with PRP and stem cells that will actually regenerate versus cover-up the pain and the problems. Yes, I realize money is a factor for most and they may not be able to afford it all, but I still present to everybody like they are my mom and that they need it all (if they do and would benefit).

From there, I am able to be an assistant buyer and find her a budget that provides her the most value. We present it all because we believe the more the patient commits to, the greater their chance of success. It is important to not make judgments on what people can afford, as that is a personal projection of money issues. People are searching for answers and the cost of not having health is the most expensive burden one can carry. Our system finds money for them and helps them identify where they can afford different treatment options by exchanging items of less value for the transformation they desire.

Whether it's sales with my team members or personal relationships, we must learn how to communicate effectively, and problem solve on how to reach the desired outcome. A gap needs to be established and agreed upon, otherwise it will not happen. Communication should be at a sixth-grade level and it needs to be clear. A confused mind never buys so you should be talking about two to three options maximum, and we should have clear next steps, accountabilities and expectations with a timeline for different objectives if we are effectively communicating.

We know most medical professionals have good intentions for patients, but do not see themselves as salespeople. You're a moral and ethical person. Our job is to get patients better, but sick patients plus a good doctor does not equal a healthy patient. We are responsible to get our patients healthy but that is derived from a professional who will not quit in their attempt to help patients change their lives. We need a smart doctor who can influence patients and never give up on finding solutions that work for the patient. You inspire and motivate action.

I know you probably do not like sales, but new patients are needed for your business. But new patients do not equal success - compliant patients do. So, you have to be able to 'sell' them on being compliant to the programs. Rarely does one treatment, procedure fix or test expose the root cause of the diagnosis. You have to be able to explain the journey and possibilities to be explored and the work to be done to fix the root cause.

To get the patient compliant with your program, you must understand their psychology and mindset. You have to be able to coach, emotionally connect, inspire and hold patients accountable to possible solutions. They have to believe they can do it. You have to invite them into a comprehensive and individualized treatment plan, formalize the relationship with a sale, then coach them to adhere to the result they just said they wanted. All of this is selling, whether we like it or not. If you are not able to do this at a high level, you need practice, or you can hire a case manager who can handle the money, coaching and accountability conversations.

Your patient is sick and tired of being sick and tired. They are in pain, which makes them frustrated. They are looking for answers that no one has figured out and they're looking for a professional who can provide hope and new solutions that differ from the traditional attempts. They are searching for a professional who is compassionate, and who will take the time to listen and educate them on all their options. They desire a provider with a good reputation. They are seeking a specialist and not a generalist.

One of my mentors, Ed Rush, taught me what myths people need to overcome regarding sales to take action. Now I want you to overcome the myths on what you believe to be true about sales. Earlier, I mentioned persuasion versus manipulation. What is persuasion versus manipulation? It is only how you are presenting, if people are not buying at this point. I used to think if I did a good presenting, then people would tell me it was inspiring and loaded with great information - but I was confused because they did not buy.

So, if the information is good, why don't you have more patients? It is because you have not yet become an expert at communicating. Many people get frustrated by those having big success in selling inferior products or services. We also let the scam artist who can market and sell continue to grow when we do not learn to put our message out there. If you're good at what you provide, then you are obligated to help inform your prospective patients on what to look out for in the marketplace. What is persuasion versus manipulation? Persuasion is over-delivering and under-promising. Manipulation is over-promising and under-delivering. Persuasion is the ability to get people to take action and it's the number one transformation and money-making skill on earth.

The second myth is '*I do not want to be too sales-y*'. Most people picture a used car sales dealer when they think about sales. At the end of the day, people are not in the car lot if they do not want a car. You may view sales as pushy, bossy, deceptive, greedy, uncaring, pulling one over, lies, untrustworthy or selfish. If any of your thoughts are these, go back to myth number one. You do not have to give false scarcity or outlandish promises, as that is not good practice. Just tell the truth. State there is no time to wait as pain is the most expensive burden to carry. Ask them the cost of not making changes that will better their life. The cost of doing nothing is too high, in case you have not figured it out yet. This is just a state of mind and it's why I am successful getting people to take action. When I believe our product is a solution for them, I let them know and, if not, I will tell them they are not a good fit. I am going to continue to develop my communication, persuasion and ability to influence and sell prospects and patients on what they need and want.

The third myth is that money is not important to me. The only people who say this are the ultra-rich and poor. If you do not like money, it is difficult to have the income freedom and impact you desire in your practice. You need money to support the causes you believe in - that also changes the world.

We have given back so much to our community this year and it's because we have a good relationship with money. It is part of our purpose and giving back is a great feeling. It was a great night last year when we were able to write a $15,000 check to Place of Hope. This year at our annual Cash Practice Success Summit, we are sponsoring the Hope Field House - a mission offering underserved children recreational opportunities. We will be donating 10 percent of all the revenue each year directly to our cause of choice.

The last myth is that my service speaks for itself. I only know a couple of these people who do not have to market or sell. They have become a category of one. They have a waiting list that is never-ending. Dr. James Andrews, who is a big advocate of regenerative medicine, doesn't have to market or sell anymore because he is known as a category of one. He still produces content and has a desire to educate consumers because it's part of his calling. When you work on educating consumers and providing information on alternative solutions, you are persuading people to look at their health differently.

To persuade effectively, you need to view yourself accurately. Your market needs to view you accurately by fully letting them see what the benefit is for them. Lastly, you need your market to view your product, service or transformation accurately.

5 Reasons People Buy

We, ultimately, need to know why people buy because everybody is shopping the outcomes. We all have the same exact problems and inability to deal with our current problems to immediately solve them. We are all willing to pay for speed or specific outcomes. Before I communicate our services to prospects, it is important to know that there are five reasons that people buy.

1) It's a product or service that gives them hope. That your weight loss program actually may work. That your stem cell procedure may be able to allow a person to still play the sport they love.

2) They have a fear of loss. A diabetic patient with heart disease may realize that if they don't start exercising, their family may be without them soon. That if I do not do this, I am going to miss out on something good, or I will lose my ability to live without something.

3) They have desire to gain. I will be able to pass the military testing, gain a desired position, or attract a person of interest.

4) To avoid pain. Their knee is causing significant pain.

5) They desire happiness. Simply stated, if a product or service can provide happiness, people are willing to part with their money.

Your job is to transfer your feelings. If you believe that regenerative, functional or lifestyle medicine is the best solution, you can't let people searching for outcomes walk out your door for an inferior service. Transference of feelings can be bad if your mindset is not on-point. If you do not invest in yourself, if you can't afford to pay for those services, or would not make the same decision if you were in their position, then it is likely you will struggle to sell cash-pay services.

Help People Find Funding For Their Predictable Transformation

When I first started personal training, I had the wrong relationship with money. I didn't sell big transformational packages partly because I only made $20K myself and did not feel people would be able to afford these large purchases. Because I was able to be successful on my own, I told myself they could be as well. Now I am able to share with prospects that you have to be willing to exchange something of less value for something of more value.

I take the time to go through everything they are spending extra money on that will not help them reach their desired outcome. How often are they eating out and how much does it cost them monthly? How much money are they spending on drinking or drugs? How are they making lifestyle choices? What are the non-essentials they are spending money on in their life? I simply ask them, are you willing to make changes and exchange those dollars for the next six months to lose the 25 pounds that you desire?

Those habits, if continued, will prevent them from the outcome they seek and, regardless, have to be managed properly. If they say no, we do what we call a push-away. "*I do not know that we are able to get results without making some lifestyle sacrifices and I am not sure this is the right fit for you at this time.*" When you are not selling them and, instead, you are qualifying them, the psychology in the patient changes and they end up selling themselves to you.

We find them the money necessary to enroll in our program and see if they have the means for our lowest point of entry before we ever provide options. We also assume nobody came expecting our programs to be free. We know they can afford our programs by making lifestyle changes. As an entry point, they can probably afford a greater transformation program as well.

After we take their History of Present Illness (HPI), we identify their gaps. Ninety percent of your conversation should be on the outcome of transformation and result if the program is followed. Therefore, after you have done a great job of listening to their HPI, and you have done a thorough exam, you should be talking about the gap, intake, exam or what their tests showed.

For example, if you perform a diagnostic ultrasound and you identify a meniscus tear, then show them that. If they agree with the gap, then it is time to talk about the transformation possibilities, the solution, the emotion, what they desire, the energy and excitement of your solution, and be sure to replicate the words that they use. Only 10 percent of the conversation should center around your service delivery and features of your program.

This means people do not buy the plane when they go to Hawaii - they buy the experience. A travel agent does not talk about the seats, the type of plane they will be on, that there's 38 inches between the two seats, and that the plane has a world-class engine. You are not going to sell Hawaii talking about the delivery, even though it is a part of the package of what you are buying. You are buying the experience and the outcome that you will remember for the rest of your life. You talk about the beautiful sunsets, beaches, the beauty and the memories your family will remember for the rest of their lives. That is what people want - the end result. We have to be a good listener and echo their words, if you feel you can help them.

There are other numerous communication pearls that can turn you into a life-changer that pushes people into action. Phrases such as: "*We don't make promises, but I can predict doing nothing will not make your situation any better*" or "*Ninety percent of our patients see positive outcomes such as reduction of pain, range of motion improvements, or complete resolution of symptoms. Those who do not respond well need a second injection and continued lifestyle changes determine if your body's own ability to heal is possible.*"

You can use case managers to follow up with patients. We use patient advocates and regenerative specialists, health coaches and a systematic approach to follow up with patients who go forward with treatment and those that do not. We have found what does not work is professionals who perform one-and-done treatments, not prescribing long-term treatment plans, not telling patients everything that it takes, not listening to the patients, and not inviting people for transformation.

What does work are professionals who do what needs to be done, prescribe what needs to be prescribed, and orders tests that need to be ordered. Do not let the thought of cost to your patient interfere with your decision-making process. If they have come to you for help, it is a disservice not to allow them to choose to work with you to transform their health.

It is time to start being strategic in your practice. Your success is your ability to make the decision to improve your skills. Success is yours by learning, being dedicated to practicing communication mastery, and keeping your focus on successfully transforming your patients' lives. Influence is your ability to get someone to do something that they want on some level. Time and money has nothing to do with what they want - their commitment will initiate their transformation. Your job is to simply get out of the way at that point.

CHAPTER 6: THE MEDICAL FITNESS PILLAR

"The best doctor gives the least medicine." - Benjamin Franklin

The current state and uncertainty that the healthcare system brings has required diligent focus from physicians, private practices and hospital systems to formulate solutions. The existing structure brings intense challenges for private practices to survive. With rising healthcare costs, reimbursements continue to experience cuts, leaving many medical systems vulnerable.

The upside is that there is a large opportunity for practices to protect their future by adding cash-based models of lifestyle medicine and preventable care to their current standard. This model will restore health in patients and it is proving to mature at an extraordinary pace. In 2018, CMS will release "The Diabetes Prevention Program" (DPP), creating the first opportunity for preventative services, such as personal training, health coaching and wellness services to be covered by insurance.

The obesity epidemic and the incidence of disease and injury have forced the need for a preventable, medically-integrated and outcome-based model of medical fitness. Today's crisis leads to an urgent new paradigm in healthcare delivery that will combat the rise in chronic disease and associated healthcare costs. It is our focus, along with numerous other affiliations such as the Medical Fitness Association and Medical Fitness Network, to facilitate bridging the gap between evidence-based health-centered treatment and long-term disease prevention strategies.

We Incorporated Medical Fitness to Create Change in a Broken System

The six-step "Medical Fitness I.M.P.A.C.T. Plan" we created at Rejuv Medical is the future of medicine. In nine years, we have grown leaps and bounds, and are building momentum for a viable and long-lasting entity that will help society rebound from the current healthcare crisis. I found that we can market medical fitness completely differently from traditional medical practices. The world is hungry for healthy weight loss and people are fed up with the quick-fix gimmicks. Medically supervised weight loss and fitness programs created by a physician have a unique selling position that puts us in a category of one. It lends credibility that attracts those who have struggled to gain control over their weight for years.

It has been just under nine years since my first day of work. We have now improved the lives of more than 3,000 patients. In the first 10 months before our standalone location, we were profitable because there was very little overhead. When we moved to our 6,000 square foot center, we had nearly $180,000 in losses - as a standalone, due to the build-out, new equipment, additional administrative support and day-to-day overhead expenses.

Even though we lost a third of our revenues from insurance companies dropping our contracts, as well as from the build-out expenses and equipment acquisition cost, the motivator was that the investment paid for itself. The new patients who came for the weight loss and fitness program generated over $300,000 in new revenue from the referrals to the clinic. It took exactly one year and one month to have our first profitable month as a standalone fitness facility. Still to this day, we have utilized our fitness facility as the entry point and marketing focus to bring in new patients to our clinic who are ready for positive long-term lifestyle change.

In a very short time frame, both our fitness center and clinic grew at a rapid pace. The original goal was not to create a master plan of driving fitness patients to our clinic. We originally developed ourselves to be a concierge service to Dr. Baumgartner's patients with the plan to improve outcomes, and not specifically to use it as a means to attract new patients to the clinic. We instantly recognized that this was the type of program that the community was seeking. The medical integration created trust and comfort for those who would not normally join a gym. We knew we could optimize our patients' results with functional medicine and safely progress patients' suffering from pain and degeneration. Communication between the medical and fitness staff allows us to provide the maximum safety, progression and results by integrating our care.

Naturally, we faced our share of ample mistakes along the way. Countless hours were spent developing our program from scratch and we exhausted an ocean of money on ineffective advertising. We set up pricing structures incorrectly, and had no continuity built into our programs. Blocks of sessions were sold rather than putting clients on automatic draft or long-term life-changing programs.

Years in medical school taught Dr. Baumgartner to be a great doctor. My schooling gave me the foundation of basic business management. Like many new adventures, we were not the most advanced when it came to building a business. Over time, our model has grown following the philosophy of adding different sources of revenue to the business model once one sector is performing well. Positioning all your eggs in one basket makes you vulnerable. It's all about creating multiple streams of income and increasing the value of each patient while maximizing each patient's health outcome.

There are going to be swings in the economy, this we know, but you need to prepare yourself with a recession-proof business, so you will keep sailing no matter what happens. With the uncertainty of the healthcare reform, it is critical that we take protective measures to ensure the success and livelihood of our practices. Devising a strong blend of cash-paying services, along with insurance-contracted services, is critical to your survival in today's competitive healthcare business environment.

Traditionally, medical services tend to slow a little in the first month or two after the New Year due to insurance deductibles resetting. Developing multiple streams of income makes for a stable system throughout the year, no matter the season, whether Dr. Baumgartner is seeing patients or is out of the office educating and sharing at speaking engagements. Today our practice can survive all on its own with the current team we have, even if Dr. Baumgartner were to remove himself from the practice.

	2009	2010	2011	2012	2013	2014	2015	2016
Total Sales(Revenue)	1,343,922.33	2,166,000.03	2,443,240.36	3,061,523.14	3,007,195.42	3,322,826.00	5,059,327.00	6,760,562.00
Fitness (Revenue)	NA	131,210.82	314,121.34	675,219.12	666,448.89	804,903.00	1,232,955.00	1,418,107.00
Fitness Referral	NA	107,890.00	206,040.45	345,678.90	392,825.00	588,220.00	928,265.68	1,169,053
Net Income	459,688.90	211,894.25	150,103.26	272,017.54	47,304.00	(225,000.00)	61,758.92	159,012.00
Net Income + Salary	569,288.90	701,469.09	566,347.76	705,597.85	387,304.00	115,000.00	401,758.00	479,000.00

In January, the Weight Loss & Performance Center netted $50,551.75. A potential slow month at the clinic due to deductibles resetting can still be a very lucrative month. Dr. Baumgartner could have taken the whole month off. The practice is still making an impact in the community and generating an income without the need to have the medical providers be present at all times. This also creates an environment for higher retention due to provider satisfaction when having multiple team members.

Our success to date has been due to initial sacrifice through intense and extreme working hours from Dr. Baumgartner and I, along with a team that has continuously supported our mission to make an undeniable impression in healthcare. I look at how important each of those team members have been in our journey. Without several of them, their sacrifices and investment of time in our organization, I would not be writing this book.

We have made our program as turn-key as possible to help other medical systems replicate our model. Before any practice considers this model, a Discovery Call is made with the potential candidate consisting of a comprehensive assessment to determine the most effective action steps. We have learned a practice must be successful in their core focus before adding additional services.

The Benefits of The Medical Fitness I.M.P.A.C.T. Plan

1) Create real health for patients by aiding to reverse chronic disease and improve outcomes in clinical settings.
2) Make an undeniable difference in your community and, thus, be the "go-to" within your niche.

3) Lead the mission to change the direction of our healthcare crisis by being proactive through adding conservative, integrative and preventive medicine through nutrition and fitness services.

4) Have a mission and purpose-driven team that is on fire to make a difference.

5) It is easy to add to any current clinic size if there is existing office or PT space.

6) Low overhead options and no risk propositions.

7) You don't have to build It. The Implementer leads the implementation.

8) Build a practice that isn't fully dependent on provider income.

9) Decrease the need for medications that don't address the root of several medical issues.

10) Diversify and build a practice that is cash-model friendly.

11) The best solution for outcome and bundled payment models.

12) Create constant new referrals to their existing practice.

13) Incredible marketing and patient attractor for your practice.

14) Highly motivated population increases compliance and outcomes.

15) Extreme cross-referral synergy that benefits all departments.

16) Medical fitness patients become lifelong patients. Because you change their lives, your patients will become raving fans.

17) Medical clinics can leverage a position of authority to attract new patients into the practice.

18) Complement a current medical practice to increase ancillary revenue.

19) Stay a step ahead of the competition by being the first in your area in the medical fitness market. Differentiation and out-innovating your competitors is essential in a saturated niche.

20) For the first-time, CMS will utilize the "Diabetes Prevention Program." This insurance program will cover wellness services for patients with prediabetes, diabetes and metabolic syndrome.

CHAPTER 7: THE INTEGRATION PILLAR

"Physicians sometimes tend to be cautious, so they miss out on a lot of opportunities." - Leigh Page, MS, Medscape (from the article *Six Ancillary Services Worth Considering*), October 15, 2012

Michael Janetis walked into our practice looking to improve his health. He was hopeful we could solve his 20-year shoulder and sternum issues through medical fitness; even after a recommendation to start in the clinic, he still just wanted fitness. Over the years, he had put on 40 pounds. Even though we were providing safe and progressive workouts, he experienced a flare-up and it took him back out of the gym. He finally agreed to see Dr. Baumgartner.

When he first came in, we put him on the Rejuv 4 Life Meal plan aimed at reducing inflammation within his body and providing a diet that fit his lifestyle. Dr. Baumgartner performed PRP and put him in a sling for two weeks. We reviewed his labs - he was low in testosterone and vitamin D. He was prescribed three months of physical therapy, two times a week. Three months later, he was back in the gym working out and never had an issue again. He lost 50 pounds in the process and now looks great and is feeling 100 percent. He has been an advocate and a leader for hundreds of others on social media on how to transform your live with regenerative healthcare.

Amazing transformations like Michael's happen every day when we integrate people through our system. When they experience all we have to offer and they do the necessary work to make changes in their lives, there have been few we are not able to help. What are your systems and ancillary revenue sources to improve outcomes, efficiencies, save time and money while maximizing communication in your practice? How can your practice communicate together and provide the ultimate patient care because integrated practices that communicate with each other are few and far between?

The Cleveland Clinic, which is touted as one of the largest integrative medical facilities in the world, still operates in silos. The comprehensive care model in most large systems is very disconnected. Our integrated model is about combining and allowing our systems to communicate with each other, providing unified communications within staff and educational resources to our patients so they understand the next levels of care to improve their outcomes.

A documented and visual system that allows patients to discover their gaps by simple questionnaires allows patients to see the importance of integration. We have integrated communication platforms that allow the providers, trainers and health coaches to share patient data so there is continuity of care and allows for all elements of integration to be explored and communicated.

We use insurance as an entry point for office visits, general labs and traditional care. During every visit, we present cash-pay services that have shown to be more effective at restoring and regenerating health. We have internal systems to escalate people to the services that we believe will transform their lives. We teach our hybrid model to practices who use insurance as an entry point. Even if people say no to the cash option initially, we use a free online membership site for each new patient loaded with physician education and meal plans and cookbooks to help them optimize their outcomes. We also start the indoctrination process to educate and seed them on the potential benefits of our other service opportunities for transformation.

Medical Fitness Wellness Program

How to access Rejuv University:

www.RejuvUniversity.com

Username: guest

Password: changemylife

320.217.8480 | www.RejuvMedical.com

Medical Fitness Test Drive

○ 2 Week Free Pass Includes:

- Infrared Sauna
- Studio Classes
- Open Gym Access
- Educational Seminars
- Childcare
- Towel Service

❋ Health Assessment

❋ Functional Movement Screening

❋ Customized Medical Fitness Sessions

Provide Care Beyond the Room

Not only is an integrated system about superior patient care, it is about helping you create impact and income without only your time as a provider in the patient visit room. Are you using digital products, offline books, video education, physical products and offering corporate wellness contracts? Are you adding additional ancillary revenue sources or offering affiliate programs that help you make more income while maximizing your patients' outcomes? If not, you are leaving a lot on the table. This chapter is going to be based on how we operate and integrate data internally, what we offer internally, and then external integration on how we get patients to experience everything we offer to achieve world-leading outcomes.

The first element is internal integration. Many providers ask how we get our gym fitness system to integrate with our EHR (electronic health record system). This has been a consistent effort on how we create systems that allow each department access to patient information so we can provide the best care possible. On the fitness side, we use soap notes and created bio scores that help identify internal and external biometrics that allow us to communicate with patients about their health. When patients enter the clinic first, we use questionnaire forms that identify whether patients have gaps in their diet, hormones and active daily living habits.

Last year, one of our Regenerative Communication Specialists came to my office to express an exciting call he received. He is responsible for facilitating calls and conversing prospective patients through Rejuv's C.F.A.N. process to ensure we communicate our method for producing the best possible healing outcomes. He said, "*John Doe called and asked what our cost was for our Bone Marrow Stem Cell Treatment.*"

His experience told him not to jump right into pricing for a few reasons. The first is we are not the "bargain price" in our area by any stretch, for any of our services, and our unique differentiating factor is not our pricing. Beyond that, reducing our value to a price tag simply makes our services a commodity - and commodities can be replaced.

Secondly, if we do this for any service that we offer, we may not qualify that this prospective patient is a good fit for our practice without fully listening to the patient and asking the right questions. We clearly communicate with our patients, team and business affiliates what it takes to achieve the best results, promotion, raises and success someone is seeking. We have no obstacle training a patient who is just looking to get moving, as any positive change is a step in the right direction. However, the greatest results come from behavior, nutritional and mindset changes. Last, and most importantly, our value comes from integrating all our departments to create a comprehensive approach and patient-centered care.

The specialist asked the patient, "*Do you have recent blood labs in the last six months, x-rays and/or MRI images so we can review your candidacy for success with our treatments?*" The person asked what these would be used for, so the specialist replied, "*the labs will determine if your cell health and hormones are in the right balance to create the proper healing environment and your images will be reviewed by Dr. Baumgartner to see if you are an appropriate candidate for this treatment. He prefers if you are close enough to receive an exam and full history evaluation first because, in many instances, some of our insurance covered treatments like injections, physical therapy and proper eating can eliminate the need for this procedure. For now, I would like to send you the information on our C.F.A.N. process to maximize healing outcomes and access to our Rejuv University that has an anti-inflammatory cookbook, meal plans and physician education in preparation for your office visit. Would you like to schedule an office visit to review your labs and for a full exam so we can go over all your options?"* Mr. Doe replied, *"Wow! I have called several places and no one asked me these questions and review with me what it would take for me to be successful. You didn't even try to sell me your stem cell procedure and possibly cost yourself a good sale as this is what I thought I needed right away. What does next week look like for an appointment?"*

Cell Health
Functional Movement
Articulation
Nerves

- SUPPLEMENTS
- FUNCTIONAL MEDICINE
  - HORMONE OPTIMIZATION
  - MIRCRONUTRIENT BALANCING
  - STRESS MANAGEMENT
  - SLEEP
  - TOXINS
- REJUV 4 LIFE NUTRITION
- MEDICAL FITNESS

- BRACING
- LEVELS OF FITNESS
- PHYSICAL THERAPY
- FMS RESTORATION
- PROLOTHERAPY
- PRP
- STEM CELLS
- LUBRICATION (KNEE)

- TOPICAL CREAMS
- NERVE BLOCKS
- EPIDURALS

Printed Name:_____
DOB:_____
Date:_____

 **Rejuv** INTAKE SCREEN
MEDICAL

CELL HEALTH	YES	NO
1. Do you feel more tired or fatigued than you think you should?		
2. Do you feel you could be eating healthier and want to learn more about nutrition?		
3. Have you gained unwanted weight or want to lose weight?		
4. Do you feel like your hormones are not in balance?		
5. Would you like healthier skin with a change in texture, tone and quality?		
6. Do you feel you would like to perform at a higher level?		

FUNCTIONAL MOVEMENT	YES	NO
1. Do you feel you would benefit from exercising at a more regular interval?		
2. Do you feel stiff or that you have lost range of motion in your joints or spine?		
3. Do you feel weak or vulnerable in any muscle groups?		
4. Would you like more instruction on how to keep your body and spine healthy?		

ARTICULATION	YES	NO
1. Do you have unwanted pain in your joints or spine?		
2. Have you been told you need or want to avoid surgery for any orthopedic conditions?		
3. Do you have past injuries or surgeries that are still affecting you?		
4. Do you have arthritis that is limiting your abilities or is painful?		

NERVE HEALTH	YES	NO
1. Do you have numbness or tingling in your body?		
2. Have you had any injury to your spine or peripheral nerves?		
3. Do you have any pain that radiates in your body?		
4. Do you have frequent headaches?		
5. Do you feel your body responds slower and more sluggish then desired?		

Do you have other questions or areas the you would like Rejuv Medical to assist you?

_____

_____

Using these internal systems, we show our patients what it takes to restore and regenerate health. We teach physicians in our mastermind how to attain the skills to add different ancillary revenue sources. Within the C.F.A.N. model, C. stands for cell health F. is functional movement, A. is for articulation and N. is for nerve health. The image above goes into our EHR with all of our services that are offered in each one of these areas. This way each new patient is given a treatment plan based on their gaps and we are able to communicate that to the patient based off their own intake form.

So, when somebody comes into any one of our main departments, whether it is fitness, regenerative, orthopedics or medical fitness, we start automating emails to help explain about everything it takes to get the best outcome through email automation. Communication of the gaps is really important to new patients. When they are coming for one service and decide not to do the entire program, they are still prospects for each additional service we offer. What this means is when we continue to educate and give offers for additional services, they will eventually integrate throughout our entire system. When we continue to communicate how they can get better outcomes, the more they experience our additional services. If somebody comes back for an injection because they still have knee pain but they did not exercise, improve their eating habits or do any meal plans, we are able to see that they did not do what we said it takes to get the best outcome. We reiterate that when people do work in all the areas, we are better able to deliver a consistent and repeatable outcome.

If you're interested in the medical research and treatment plan using the C.F.A.N. method, be sure to check out Dr. Baumgartners bestselling book, *Regenerate: How To Restore and Regenerate health without Drugs or Surgery.*

The last component of integration is automation. You shouldn't be doing repeatable processes multiple time throughout a day if your goal is to scale and grow. Things like billing, electronic funds transfers, general education and patient information can easily be delivered through email or video platforms.

However, automation that takes away from human connection and the patient experience with systematic touch points should not be ignored or automated.

"The first rule of any technology used in a business is that automation applied to an efficient operation will magnify the efficiency. The second is that automation applied to an inefficient operation will magnify the inefficiency," - Bill Gates

CHAPTER 8: 11 'SHOULD ASK' QUESTIONS

1) For the practices that experience success, what is the most important factor for growth besides the right people who can sell and launch the program off the ground?

Building a sustainable and successful practice without proven outcomes is nearly impossible. Having the right staff and a solid marketing plan to get prospects into your funnel are the two leading factors for growth. However, those alone are simply not enough. Even with terrible marketing, your business can grow slowly as long as you are superior to anything else that exists in your marketplace. You get referrals when you get results, and this is our number one way we acquire new patients.

Being acknowledged for results helps you stand out compared to any other competition in the area. Providing extreme value and results to your patients is the biggest and most powerful factor for guaranteeing a long business life for your practice. Patients must feel welcomed, respected, loved and protected. There must be systems in place that allow your patients to get the desired results they seek. After years of practice, for me, personally, it was easy to coach people to see results. Many of my subsequent hires did not have the same skills, so I created systems and quickly shifted to employee development training programs with the basis being how to achieve results and retain patients long-term.

When we meet with patients, we must build rapport and be honest - in a very compassionate and caring manner- about the gaps they will need to fill to attain results. When someone is morbidly obese and says they just want to go once a week for just a month, I know I am failing that client by not saying they need a year-long program three times a week. Someone who is inactive and is seeing a physical therapist will not get better going once a week. We need to see them a minimum of two times a week.

Not offering up-sells and telling them the most effective, fast, and proven methods of getting results is considered not caring enough for your patient. For example, if we sell a training package and stop right there, we have not provided the most effective way to get results. After you have them committed into buying training, your next line should be, *"By the way, here are three supplements that will help you see the best results,"* or *"I know your knee hurts. I should have you meet with the doctor first."* You must advise them on what will be best and not look at it as sales. You do not need their money; remember, you truly desire them to reach their goals. It is more like being an assistant buyer and a trusted advisor vs. a salesman. It is okay if a patient chooses not to follow exactly what you recommend but, the point is, you must offer them the best path possible to reach their goal. Once you have done that, you will continue to show your value to patients. It is not just about results; it is about positively impacting lives.

2) What are the most important staffing lessons you have learned?

We have seen failure in several locations now and it was too late to help several of the people we started coaching. I can narrow it down to five reasons for the staffing failures.

1) In several instances, key providers and trainers were not paid what they believed to be fair or were unhappy with the long-term growth plan. Unfortunately, they left unethically (in my opinion) and started their own practices and took several patients and clients with them. I have an abundance mindset and know we can attract new patients when we do our job right, and I am happy as long as they are contributing to make the

world a better place. To avoid these issues, I recommend a non-disclosure as these do hold up much better by protecting your proprietary information and your patients' information. Most patients build a relationship with their provider or coach and you stand to lose patients even if they did it the right way. I recommend a proper incentive-based performance structure, a profit-sharing model, and possible ownership options once key providers have proven themselves.

2) If a team member is not successful in their role during the first three months, no matter how much you/we like them, they are not the right fit to help you grow.

3) Hiring team members without the capacity or skills to do the job at a high level because they are a relative, friend, patient or because a candidate is more affordable is not a good idea. Hire them only when they have proven capacity for success in a specific role.

4) Owners or directors that micromanage too much, especially in areas that do not require micromanaging. Having proper key performance metrics to evaluate and develop the team member is the key to finding the middle ground.

5) Lack of fluid communication, support and collaboration between team members and supervisor. Some team members cite constant pressure with minimal support.

3) What is the biggest mistake you see cash practice clinics make?

Not having a marketing budget of at least 5K per month when starting to consistently have print materials, a high-performing website, social media, networking and digital marketing budget. Not maximizing the grassroots strategies to grow outside referrals that are necessary with the launch of the program is a major oversight.

In addition, not increasing budget when a positive return is found on any marketing platform. Owners at times can view an increased budget as an expense rather than an immediate and long-term investment in growth based on positive returns.

4) How much time does the physician or owner need to be involved in marketing and management?

In the beginning, we would like participation with creating the personal marketing storyboard materials and infographics on the practices' proven process. A weekly video that can be spread across multiple platforms is something the great practices do consistently. Being involved in the weekly or monthly seminars is a solid strategy for growing your cash practice. Even if the owners and physicians do not oversee anyone, I still suggest that owners attend weekly one-hour meetings regarding key performance indicators and quarterly goals while discussing and resolving issues, as these are critical to keep the practice moving forward.

5) Am I able to bring all my staff members if we choose to work with you further?

The greater the buy-in and development of the entire organization, the greater potential for massive impact. We have detailed and advanced training for each provider, billing, IT, administrative, nursing, marketing and business development staff. We want our partners to mimic our path to success while avoiding the (many) mistakes we have made along the way.

6) Can you help me hire the right person?

We teach and have a turn-key recruiting system for each partner that's equipped with job descriptions, compensation plan options, posting templates, prescreen and interview questions, sample offer letters, suggested benefit offerings, compliance modules and where to post career opportunities. We also have independent contractors we can refer you to so you can focus on your unique abilities.

7) Will you be able to teach me everything your clinic is doing to be successful?

Absolutely! That is our main goal - to increase patient outcomes, profitability and have massive community impact, we implore you to replicate what our team has successfully created. Now nearing ten completed years in practice, our model cannot be replicated overnight. We created the "The Five Pillars of Practice Success Platform" that is designed to create a highly profitable, scalable, automated and impactful practice in three years' time.

Some groups, depending where they are at, they will be able to complete the curriculum faster and some groups may require more time. This book is based on what you need to be successful. When practices are accepted into our mastermind or licensed medical fitness program, they get everything we have created, along with in-depth curriculum, site visits and dedicated coaching and training hours.

8) What will our group have to create in addition to what comes with your program?

You will need to create your original story, mission, core values and company scorecard. To make the process easier, you will model the templates that we have created. You will be asked to share them during coaching calls, as they are needed to measure and ensure success. Creating custom videos and content will also speed the reach of your message to your community.

Each Pillar comes with worksheets, video and audio training and templates to input your unique information. To make the program integrate with your model of healthcare and current operating systems, we will work closely with your group to customize a workflow that will assist in meeting practice goals, objectives and key performance indicators.

9) How do you track success?

During the first coaching sessions, we establish projections, key performance indicators, tracking mechanisms and overall scorecards for each team member and department. You cannot manage or improve what you cannot measure. You get what you inspect, not what you expect.

10) When do you think all insurances will cover medical fitness, functional medicine or regenerative services?

I'm not sure we want that, but it looks like the writing is on the wall if the system is to change. If it does go this way, we will adjust and be happy that more people will have access to life-changing treatment options. CMS has started to cover preventative and wellness services starting this year for those meeting specific medical criteria. I believe if solid reporting and tracking metrics are established, within a three-year reporting window, this program will prove healthcare savings, medication reduction and greater chronic disease management.

I predict all insurances will cover medically-supervised training and wellness services for those in the at-risk categories in the coming years. Self-insured corporate plans have started utilizing regenerative and functional medicine models due to the significant cost savings inside their plans. States such as Arkansas and Texas have already approved regenerative treatments to be covered across the board.

11) What are the three biggest mistakes you have made?

1) Not investing in more high-level coaching and turn-key programs from the start for other department leaders. This would have saved us from several costly mistakes while, instead, developing critical skills of the leaders of our company. Each investment (besides one) has paid 10x the cost of the program. Investing in coaching is a crucial aspect of personal and professional growth in addressing current gaps.

2) The biggest mistake we made was having patients submit letters to their insurance providers regarding the cash services we provided in efforts to obtain coverage. In 2013, we lost half our insurance contracts due to this action. This nearly cost us everything because it happened right when we went into our large building. We have been back in network with all the

payors due to tracking our outcomes and our care was, ultimately, more affordable.

Unfortunately, we have helped less people due to this mistake and took a major hit to our growth projections that, at the time, we were on pace to achieve. Now we clearly have a "this is not covered" conversation with patients. We prefer shifting our practice to a larger share of cash-pay but we are now more prepared than when they were taken from us. Cash services reduce the cost of business and we believe it to be the better medicine in many instances. We like keeping insurance because many office visits, labs and traditional care that we offer is covered and they are a great place to start the indoctrination process of educating our patients on all their options.

In the future, many of the current cash services we offer could be covered as the evidence is too strong and consumers are demanding these healthcare options. We are not sure we desire that at this time as the reimbursement for PRP or stem cells may be drastically reduced when payors start covering these treatments. We are already seeing a reduction in quality when physicians and advanced care providers without the proper training are performing these procedures. The pioneers have had years of training bringing this medicine to the point it's at today.

3) Not gathering enough information about what our state paid when we opened our compounding pharmacy. We were sold a program and shown projections based on another state's contracts. We ended having to be a high-volume clinic to break-even and, as soon as it did, we lost all insurance contacts because we prescribed more compounding creams than pills or tablets. This was an unwritten rule we did not know about for pharmacies. My suggestion is to do your homework before adding ancillary revenue sources dependent on insurance to make sure what is sold in one state is the same as where you are operating. This is the one of the rare times fast action came back to bite us. We lost nearly $500K in this process. Yikes! Onward and upward.

CHAPTER 9: THE TOP 10 MOST FREQUENTLY ASKED QUESTIONS

1) What is the cost to effectively start a cash-pay clinic?

Multiple options are available when it comes to getting started. I would base this decision on several factors.

Space:

1) Can you start out by sharing space with an existing clinic? If this is the case, then the startup capital needed will be much smaller than investing in a standalone location.

2) Leasing a standalone facility will require the greatest investment but will allow the most growth potential. Try to find a space that previously had a clinic there to minimize your build-out costs. When seeking a standalone facility, it's important that you build a relationship with your realtor. Explain that you are a new facility in need of starting out with the most modest budget possible. This way they are looking for the most affordable starting point that there is on the market.

When meeting the owners of the property, it's important to let the owner know that your facility will help change the lives of many people, bring more traffic to the area, increase value and the vitality of becoming a local hotspot, bring the area more interest/referrals, and increase the facility's retention rate. Ask the owner what they feel would be fair for the startup cost. There are many other options to help with the startup costs so being resourceful will be advantageous. Many owners will pay the first and last month's rent, pay the build-out cost; anything to fill up some of their empty spaces. You can also negotiate a lower start rate that increases as your profits increase and cap off at a certain percentage.

3) Own a building and have other complementary providers so they cover the rent and you operate for free while having strong referral partnerships with one another. We know several clinics that have created similar models.

Equipment costs:

You do not have to buy everything brand-new. There are several websites that sell refurbished equipment that will get the job done while you are in startup mode. It's hard to give you an accurate cost until we know what types of services you will be offering. As revenues come in, you can add more equipment to enhance your program and offerings.

Fixed expenses:

Fixed expenses are costs of doing business, such as your rent, salaried wages, insurance, utilities, employee benefits, office expenses, advertising, telephone, internet, computers, QuickBooks, accounting, bad debt, bank charges, dues and subscriptions, conventions, workman's compensation, legal dues, repairs, maintenance and any lease on equipment.

Many entrepreneurs overlook the "costs of doing business" and do not budget appropriately - this is a leading reason many small practices and businesses fail.

Cost of goods sold:

When starting and adding providers, I recommend finding one who is willing to be compensated as they are seeing each patient until you can attract enough new patients to fill a provider fast. If you can afford a base salary to attract candidates, make sure you are fully confident in your ability to keep the new provider full.

Cost of goods sold also includes your physical goods sold, such as supplements or pro shop items, payroll tax and inventory. Cost of goods sold are not a direct expense and they should increase as you grow. Typically, I like a higher cost of goods sold if set up properly, and I look to find methods to reduce fixed expenses.

As your volume increases with goods, make sure to negotiate annually with vendors for discounts. You can find providers who are not willing to go out on their own and take the full risk of opening a practice and are eager to practice medicine of this nature. We pay 30 percent of net collections after removing all the cost of goods sold.

After reviewing the four factors above, you can better estimate how much startup capital you will need. The key factor is doing a full-projection spreadsheet if just starting out because one of the biggest mistakes I see starting practitioners make is being under-capitalized when they start, and then lack the budget for marketing which is a key element for cash practice success. Marketing is a non-negotiable investment.

If you choose to build right away, join The Small Business Association to help secure capital for your facility if you do not have the credit to secure a loan. If you are already established, it should be easy to get a business loan from your local bank. If building, there are several loans and tax incremental financing options you will want to explore to save the most money. If you have the reserve capital, it could be started with minimal start-up costs. A common monthly operating budget will be anywhere from $15k to $25k per month if properly investing in the launch of the program.

If you are starting with one of the first two options, you will not need much capital to begin. A loan or available cash flow between $50,000-$100,000 will get you the necessary equipment, cover all of your fixed expenses and your cost of goods sold. Few business models can show a profit in the first year; I suggest being prepared to not have a salary in your first year of practice. If this is not possible for you, I would only suggest going with the first option.

2) What are the Stark and anti-kickback considerations with this program?

I will assume that most people reading this book belong to a clinic or a hospital setting that may have many of the legal protections already in place. Each state is different, and it is highly recommended you seek legal counsel for the proper state and federal regulation that may be applicable to you. However, giving people options after recommendations, having correct compensation plans and not paying for referrals is easily learned. Understanding the STARK and anti-kickback regulations in your state is a necessary component with this type of model. We have assisted many to navigate through the very specific questions that need to be asked of your state attorney to help determine ancillary revenue-sharing and referral processes.

3) How soon will it take me to make money?

Depending on your start-up cost selection, I have had a few groups be profitable in month one if their marketing plans were set up before they opened or they left a traditional practice setting where a significant amount of their patients followed them.

We have customized projection forms we take our clients through based on the starting costs and growth model you choose to determine break-even points. I like to put my break-even projections at the one-year benchmark;

however, I suggest creating capital at a two-year break-even to prepare for the worst-case scenario.

Some people who are new to business are under the impression that by just opening a business, they will be profitable and making a decent living in no time. Yes, that is possible; typically, however, not always reality. Frequently, the owner will need to be paid last to properly invest in the resources required to grow a thriving business.

I also ask new practice owners to try to live a minimalist life while in the early years of business. Ask yourself: what is the essential income or money you need set aside to live off for a period of 12 months and possibly beyond? If the means are not available for you to do this, one may need to consider obtaining capital for starting their practice. Instead of pulling money away from the business, we want to add to marketing, equipment, staff and create an infrastructure that will allow you to continue to grow and create a profitable business.

I strongly believe that investing in yourself and your practice is better than putting money into savings or other investments that you do not have full control over. Even though I have contributed to several investment vehicles, I would rather invest more into myself and my company than stock in some company I do not personally belong to or have the ability to direct. I strongly state the importance of becoming confident in your ability and what you can produce. When you adopt this mindset, it can take you to the next level in a hurry.

4) Do you believe in using insurance contracts to start?

The answer is both Yes and No. When patients use clinical services, office visits and labs are typically covered. If injured, physical therapy, office visits and traditional procedures are covered if the practice carries insurance. If a patient has any diagnosis, such as obesity, diabetes or metabolic syndrome, providers can create a letter of medical necessity, so patients can use their health savings accounts or flex dollars for cash services. Many often give patients codes so they can use out-of-network benefits to utilize their insurance with many of your services, if you choose to avoid insurance altogether. Not having to deal with insurance at all is a day I look forward to; however, our facility is too large at this point to not use insurance as an entry point. If we were starting from scratch or when we open other satellites on a smaller scale, we will choose to avoid insurance contracts.

5) Will the use of your Cash Practice System help my entire practice even if I take insurance?

Yes, without a doubt. In fact, when we first perform a discovery session with potential MasterMind prospects, we need to do the practice assessment mentioned in this book to understand where you are at with your current skills and operations.

We created The Five Pillars Practice Success Platform to help any practice operate more successfully and save you thousands of hours of work as well as the coaching to avoid many of the mistakes we have made as got this all figured out. We often have people who join our program go through the first three Pillars before we encourage them to start adding cash ancillary services. All the MasterMind curriculum will lead to a viable practice that is built with a proper foundation.

6) Can I talk to others who have successfully implemented this program?

Yes, we have past graduates and current affiliates who are enthusiastic to share the success, challenges and benefits of our program. Contact us and we will put you in touch with someone of your similar specialty.

7) What are your costs if I request your services?

Most of our affiliates start by joining our MasterMind program. As of the printing of this book, our fee is $1,499.92 monthly for our coaching programs which have no long-term contracts - you can stop any time you feel have the information and skills you need. We have both an online curriculum and library so that you can systematically and quickly adjust our forms, templates and materials that you can rebrand, then implement into your clinic. This program was not designed to make us rich, rather it's to help practitioners implement a model that will redefine healthcare.

Once we have made headway and most of your foundation is in place, we start the Medical Fitness Impact Plan. The license is $15K for the "Done for You" program, coaching, customized online membership site and protected territory. If you spent three months previously coaching, we reduce your license fee by that amount. We roll over up to six months of MasterMind coaching into our Medical Fitness License. Because this is a licensed program and not a franchise, you can discontinue the coaching anytime you feel you can operate successfully on your own.

I have had two groups just buy the license as they felt they had the team to operate the program successfully on their own. Personally, I believe it is a mistake to drop after two years as my team and I continue to attend masterminds to stay current with the best marketing and automation secrets in the industry. Last year alone, I was in three different masterminds with different focuses to grow our organization and my skills. Everything we learn we bring forward to our affiliates to help redefine health worldwide as we are committed to knowledge-sharing.

We have invested thousands of hours and hundreds of thousands of dollars compiling this life-changing program. We have priced ourselves within your means. We have focused on mastering our delivery and system to better provide success for all our affiliates. From the bottom of our hearts, we thank each pioneer who has taken a leap with us, all in the effort to fix a broken healthcare system and create health in both our communities and throughout the world.

8) Do you offer a Paid in Full discount if I invest for a full year?

Anyone who pays in full receives $2k off the program investment.

9) Do you offer an out of country discount?

It is our goal to spread the Medical Fitness I.M.P.A.C.T. Plan worldwide so an affiliate in any new country other than the U.S.A. will receive a $2k discount. We currently license programs in China, Taiwan and Canada.

10) Do you offer a Referral Program?

Once we have proven our value to you and you recommend us to any clinics that join our mission, we will provide you with the first month's fees as a referral bonus. That escalates by $500 for each additional affiliate that joins on your behalf. Each of the discounts and incentives can be combined to minimize investment.

CHAPTER 10: THE PERFECT STORM

This model is truly going to revolutionize the medical field in the next ten years, while helping to change millions of patient lives for the better. It gives our team the opportunity to make a difference, which is the fulfillment we seek together at Rejuv, MedFit and HealthOvators. We continue to integrate and show you how to gain maximum skills so you can operate the same way.

Our mission is to redefine healthcare worldwide, which is done through this comprehensive integrated system. We created the Cash Practice Success Summit so we can give you the knowledge to confidently begin your journey, or prepare you for the next level of success. We want you to come to our clinic and learn the structure of The Five Pillars of Practice Success Platform so you can have the impact, income and freedom you deserve.

It is not a stretch for you to have the same success. We created a model that is repeatable, that will save you thousands of dollars, your valuable time and the emotional wear of frustration in the struggle of trying to grow your practice without the right support and structure. The time is always right now because the cost of not figuring out is too high.

There are usually four primary reasons that most people are being held back, starting with the drama and chaos in life. Another may be that you are afraid of success. Next are subconscious blocks, rooted in mindset and old patterns and perceptions. Lastly are money matters. Money has to get out of the way for you to have massive success in cash practice. Even if there is not money, you have to be resourceful. Because when you commit and pay for coaching, you are held to the fire. I invest in training because I follow my money - the same is true for others. f you don't pay for what you receive and work for, it doesn't hold the same value. I know deep down I will always have enough money for food and shelter. Therefore, to thrive, you now need to go to a value-based outcome versus cost mindset.

If you think you are held back because you do not have the time, there is no such thing as time management. You can't manage time because the clock never stops. We all have the same time in a day, but you can better manage your use of time, manage your team and open yourself to possibility. Achievers do, performers be.

I wrote the rough draft of this book in one weekend following a simple structure. Yes, its not perfect by any stretch, but I can make it much better in time. It was important to me to get this message out to you. While writing this, I was not looking at my email inbox - instead, it was about drowning out the noise. It is been insanely focused for a concentrated amount of time. Most people's phones are killing them versus being leveraged properly. I still have room to grow in this area.

If you had invested in Apple and Microsoft when the opportunity was new, you would have been rich. These opportunities do not last forever. Small windows open and they close. I believe now is the time to invest in cash-pay services.

My last ask of you is this: are you treating yourself like you are the greatest investment in the world? Your number one investment in yourself is to raise your consciousness and your capabilities. As said earlier, that takes commitment, courage, capabilities and, ultimately, confidence that you gain by investing in yourself. Being in community and having the support, accountability and structure is key to your success.

You are one move away. Do it right now and be the CEO of your life because a good strategy properly executed is the greatest competitive advantage you can provide yourself and your business. It is why we win. We take imperfect action and course-correct fast when we make a mistake - we win more than we lose. Thank you so much for reading this book.

Remember - be sure to take the Five Practice Pillars Quiz (http://www.smartbizquiztribe.com/quiz/690) so you can take advantage of the bonus 1:1 strategy call about your practice goals and how to uplevel your practice to create cash practice success.

ACKNOWLEDGEMENTS

I am grateful to acknowledge all the significant people in my life who have made me who I am today - he good and the bad. From those who have caused pain to those who believed in me, supported me and even those who compete against me, I have learned that everyone is faced with wind and storms. How we learn to navigate the for-certain stormy weather that will inevitably come is the greater opportunity to use the storm's power and energy to provide the fuel to create the life you desire.

In my first bestselling book, I skipped the acknowledgments and I feel it is important to give thanks to my parents. They provided how they knew best. I thank my mother, Chris, for caring for me and always having my back even though I had a very troubled childhood. She has gifted me with two core values that make up part of my identity today - loyalty and honesty. I also thank my father for modeling behaviors that are imperative for success and joy in knowing and having my opinion as well as hard work and kindness.

I thank the teacher who teased me in the fifth grade on top of the desk for the whole class to see. For years, it affected my confidence and self-esteem but, in the same token, gave me one of my greatest gifts. You gave me empathic powers and the burning desire to help people who are in any kind of pain.

I want to thank Phoenix Fabricators and the leaders inside who allowed me to work for an organization that has provided my family security. Not many fully understand how mentally and physically exhausting one of the hardest jobs on the planet can be for an individual and family until they experience the water tower lifestyle. It was easy for me to see that any job was going to be a breeze compared to what it takes to sustain in that industry. Water towers laid the financial foundation and work ethic that allowed me to grow and learn from in four on-and-off years of building water towers.

I thank the teachers who kicked me out of high school science, English and social studies. I especially thank my social studies teacher for telling all the people she could that I would never amount to anything and telling my friends' parents they should not let their kids be my friend.

You gave me the fuel I needed to come back from water towers to go to college and prove you wrong.

I thank all my sports teammates. Sports saved my life. They stopped the mental pain. They provided me strategy, leadership and coaching skills as well as the desire to compete and win at everything I did. My teammates gave me most of my best memories. They gave me friends for life while teaching me how to compete. A special thanks to my rugby teammate, Nate Hanline. He introduced me to the fitness industry by getting me an internship at Golds Gym after an Achilles tendon rupture due to a rugby injury. A bad injury was a catalyst for my career.

I am thankful for my former clients at Golds, Jeff and Karla, for telling me about Joel Baumgartner and telling him that I would be a great complement to his new practice.

I'm forever in debt to Dr. Baumgartner for giving me the opportunity. Investing hundreds of thousands of dollars into masterminds and coaching before we ever became partners. You provided me all the resources I needed, without second-guessing me, to help grow your vision. You gave me the tools, you stayed out of my way, never micromanaged me or held onto mistakes I made. Before I evolved, I was not good with authority, so you were just what I needed to mature correctly. I now firmly believe we all need to be held accountable by someone if we want the most out of life.

I thank my coaches and mentors. I had one bad experience, but you learn from those too. Bedros Keullian, you gave me belief in myself and your message resonated with me. If you want something, you need to make it happen. Craig Ballantyne - thank you for being truthful, bold and caring enough to tell me what I didn't like to hear but knew was truth. My thanks to Lisa Sasevich for giving me structure even though I'm a creative and visionary. I'm grateful to Mike Koenigs for changing my mind to help me believe in myself and what I was called to do. For teaching me to do less, as I would have worked myself to death without you reframing my mind. Ed Rush - thank you for teaching me how to talk to my source and eliminate the lies I have told about myself for years. You are a big part of helping me find pure joy in my life given any circumstance. And gratitude to all the other consultants and coaches who have helped us reach the point we have with less time and pain of trying to figure it out on our own.

My mastermind members. For inspiring and supporting me. My greatest friends and collaboration partners have come from masterminds and events. It is important to be in the same room of those who are doing or going in the same direction you are travelling.

I want to thank Mike Jewel, Carrie Ellis and Nate Long for being spiritual leaders in my life and leading me to the Waters church. My life transformed the day I walked into my first service. I have always had my core values that my parents instilled in me; however, my reason for existence changed that day. I thank Doug Vagle for being the spiritual leader I needed. I remember his first words. "*If you're looking for the perfect pastor, you came to the wrong place.*" It was the first time I never felt judged in a church setting (after multiple attempts). Besides the love of helping and coaching people, my initial success was to prove people wrong. Doug helped me find that my calling was far beyond myself. That everything I had experienced in my life was in preparation of what I was called to do and that all I had to do was answer the call.

I want to thank our team. I get the great reward of working with people who have big hearts and who want to change people's lives. Most days are fun when you know you're making a difference. I learned this as far back as t-ball on the playground - you are only as good as your weakest link. The bigger the mission, the more important the team. A true leader knows your ability to develop and influence others positively is the key to massive impact and sustainable success. You can only do so much as one person.

My wife and kids. Change is hard. My wife deserves the best and, at times, expects the best. The last nine years of marriage have forced me to uplevel myself in every aspect of my life. I came into the marriage broken, an addict and full of extreme behaviors. At times, I have resented the change because those sources became my safety net for dealing with my emotions and my past. Kyla, you have showed me that every change is turning me into the person I desire to be for you and our kids. I love you all more than words can express. Thank you for believing in me even when I have had self-doubt. I am forever grateful for your tireless work to raise our beautiful family. You have never given me a hard time from all the work hours and travel it has taken to grow our companies.

I want to thank all the people who helped me review and edit this book. You each helped me complete this book in short order due to the deadline and my injury. Thank you to Marissa Platz, Linda Rank, Jackie Cook, Joyce Rice, Lynn Scheurell and my wife. Thank you from the bottom of my heart. This would not have been ready for publishing without your help.

Last, but not least, I need to give it all to my source in God and Jesus Christ. How I'm alive is only by your doing. Thank you for providing me with everything I could ever need and more. How you have showed me that I am capable of all through you. For showing yourself to me when I push beyond your plan for me. Thank you for slowing me down when I needed to see differently. Thank you for the skills you have given me to develop and the purpose you have laid clearly on my heart. Thank you for giving me joy and peace of understanding no matter what cards are dealt. Thanks for giving me faith and hope for all possibilities.

ABOUT JR BURGESS

JR Burgess, M.S. is the CEO of MedFit and Rejuv Medical. He is also a husband, father, coach, two-time #1 bestselling author and international speaker. JR and Dr. Joel Baumgartner partnered to innovate a healthcare model that reverses and prevents chronic pain and disease. Their  regenerative healthcare model includes non-surgical orthopedics, functional and primary care.

Successful outcomes have been proven to be driven by medical fitness. JR and Dr. Baumgartner believe that healthcare without exercise and solid nutrition as the foundation, is not healthcare. They have played an integral role in replicating the proven model in more than 60 clinics worldwide. Each clinic aiming at redefining healthcare, empowering medical leaders and patients to co-create health and impact the world.

JR wrote the bestselling book, Medical Fitness Impact Plan, which continues to be a resource for practice owners and wellness professionals who are consciously choosing to build their businesses.

JR lives in Minnesota with his beautiful wife and four amazing children. He gives gratitude daily for the challenges that, ultimately, made him who he is today.

You can reach JR through:

Website: https://www.RejuvMedical.com

Facebook: https://www.facebook.com/RejuvMedical/

LinkedIn: https://www.linkedin.com/in/jr-burgess-36908846/

ONE LAST THING...

If this book was helpful and gave you the structure and encouragement you needed to move forward, please don't let my message be one of the industry's best-kept secrets. I would greatly appreciate a review on Amazon, or an introduction to your group or association. My goal is to get the message in this book to as many medical leaders as possible. I believe HealthOvators like you are the key to redefining health care.

www.CashPracticeSuccessBook.com

99306257R00140

Made in the USA
Lexington, KY
17 September 2018